CW00821339

Bond

English
Assessment Papers

12⁺–13⁺ years
Book 1

Wendy Wren

Nelson Thornes

Published in 2007 by:
Nelson Thornes Ltd
Delta Place
27 Bath Road
CHELTENHAM
GL53 7TH
United Kingdom

11 12 13 14 / 10 9 8 7 6 5

A catalogue record for this book is available from the British Library

ISBN 978 0 7487 8478 3

Page make-up by GreenGate Publishing Services, Tonbridge, Kent

Printed and bound in Eygpt by Sahara Printing Company

Acknowledgements

The authors and publishers wish to thank the following for permission to use
copyright material:

page 2 extract from 'My Great Aunt Appearing Day' by John Prebble, published
by Secker & Warburg. Reprinted by permission of The Random House Group
Ltd; page 35 extract from 'My Family and other Animals' by Gerald Durrell.
Reproduced with permission of Curtis Brown Group Ltd, London on behalf of
the Estate of Gerald Durrell. Copyright © Gerald Durrell 1956; page 9 extract
from 'Harbinger of death in steep decline' by Lewis Smith. Reproduced with
permission of The Times / NI Syndication; page 22 extract from 'The Discovery
of the Tomb of Tutankhamen' by Howard Carter and A C Mace. Reproduced with
permission of Dover Publications 1977; page 16 extract from 'Lord of the Flies'
by William Golding. Reproduced with permission of Faber and Faber Ltd, 1977.

Every effort has been made to trace the copyright holders, but if any have been
inadvertently overlooked the publishers will be pleased to make the necessary
arrangement at the first opportunity.

Before you get started

What is Bond?

This book is part of the Bond Assessment Papers series for English, which provides **thorough and continuous practice of key English skills** from ages five to thirteen. Bond's English resources are ideal preparation for SATs exams, preparation for the 11+ and higher selective school entrance exams.

What does this book cover and how can it be used to prepare for exams?

English Assessment Papers 12⁺-13⁺ are intended as practice for 12+ and 13+ exams. The coverage is matched to the National Curriculum, so will provide invaluable preparation in the run-up to Key Stage 3 SATs. They can also be used for very advanced practice for selective exams at 11. Each paper practises comprehension, spelling, grammar and vocabulary work. It is outside the scope of this book to practise extended and creative writing skills. *Bond The secrets of Writing* provides full coverage of writing skills.

What does the book contain?

- **10 papers** – each one contains 100 questions.

- **Tutorial links throughout** – 📖 – this icon appears in the margin next to the questions. It indicates links to the relevant section in *How to do ... 11+ English*. Our invaluable subject guide offers explanations and practice for all core question types that are commonly found on 11+, 12+ and 13+ exam papers.

- **Scoring devices** – there are score boxes in the margins and a Progress Chart on page 68. The chart is a visual and motivating way for children to see how they are doing. It also turns the score into a percentage that can help decide what to do next.

- **Next Steps Planner** – advice on what to do after finishing the papers can be found on the inside back cover.

- **Answers** – located in an easily-removed central pull-out section. If you lose your answers, please email cservices@nelsonthornes.com for another copy.

How can you use this book?

One of the great strengths of Bond Assessment Papers is their flexibility. They can be used at home, in school and by tutors to:

- set **timed formal practice tests** – allow about 50 minutes per paper in line with standard entrance exam demands. Reduce the suggested time limit by five minutes to practise working at speed.

- provide **bite-sized chunks** for regular practice.

- **highlight strengths and weaknesses** in the core skills.

- identify **individual needs**.

- set **homework**.

It is best to start at the beginning and work through the papers in order. If you are using the book as part of a careful run-in to an exam, we suggest that you also have three other essential Bond resources close at hand:

How to do ... 11+ English: the subject guide that explains the key question types practised in this book. Use the cross-reference icons to find the relevant sections.

The secrets of Comprehension: the practical handbook that clearly shows children how to read and understand the text, understand the questions and assess their own answers.

The secrets of Writing: the essential resource that explains the key components of successful writing.

See the inside front cover for more details of these books.

What does a score mean and how can it be improved?

It is unfortunately impossible to guarantee that a child will pass a 12+ or 13+ exam if they achieve a certain score on any practice book or paper. Success on the day depends on a host of factors, including the scores of the other children sitting the test. However, we can give some guidance on what a score indicates and how to improve it.

If children colour in the Progress Chart on page 68, this will give an idea of present performance in percentage terms. The Next Steps Planner inside the back cover will help you to decide what to do next to help a child progress. It is always valuable to go over wrong answers with children. If they are having trouble with a particular topic or skill, follow the tutorial links to *How to do ... 11+ English* for step-by-step explanations and further practice.

Don't forget the website...!

Visit www.bond11plus.co.uk for lots of advice, information and suggestions on everything to do with Bond and helping children to do their best.

Key words

Some special words are used in this book. You will find them in **bold** each time they appear in the Papers. These words are explained here.

abbreviation — a word or words which is/are shortened

abstract noun — a noun showing ideas, actions or qualities *dignity*

active verb — form of a verb showing when the main person or thing does the action *he took it*

adjectival clause — a clause giving information about a noun or pronoun

adjectival phrase — a group of words describing a noun

adjective — a word that describes somebody or something

adverb — a word that gives extra meaning to a verb

adverbial clause — a clause giving extra meaning to the main verb in a sentence

adverbial phrase — a phrase giving information about how, when, why and with whom something happens

antonym — a word with a meaning opposite to another word *hot – cold*

clause — a section of a sentence with a verb

collective noun — a word referring to a group *swarm*

definition — a meaning of a word

diminutive — a word implying smallness *booklet*

direct speech — words which show when someone is actually speaking

expression — a particular phrase or set used to express something

homophone — a word that has the same sound as another but a different meaning or spelling *right/write*

metaphor — an expression in which something is described in terms usually associated with another *the sky is a sapphire sea*

noun — a word for somebody or something

passive verb — form of a verb showing when the main person or thing has the action done to it *it was taken by him*

phrase — a group of words that act as a unit

plural — more than one *cats*

prefix — a group of letters added to the beginning of a word *un, dis*

preposition — a word that relates other words to each other *the book on the table*

pronoun — a word used to replace a noun *them*

reported speech — words which report something spoken after it has happened

root word — a word to which prefixes or suffixes can be added to make other words *quickly*

sentence — a unit of written language which makes sense by itself

simile — an expression to describe what something is like *as cold as ice*

singular — one *cat*

suffix — a group of letters added to the end of a word *ly, ful*

superlative — describes the limit of a quality (adjective or adverb) *most/least or shortest*

synonym — a word with the same or very similar meaning as another word *quick – fast*

verb — a 'doing' or 'being' word

My Great-Aunt Appearing Day

I was thirteen when I first heard of my great-aunt Appearing Day.

Late one afternoon, shortly after my birthday, my father discovered me at play with a crude bow and arrow I had fashioned for myself. For some minutes he watched me from the kitchen door, his hands thrust into the front pockets of his check trousers, his eyes squinting against the sun. Then he called me to him   5
abruptly, and when I came he took the toy from my hands. I waited, expecting a rebuke, but instead he slipped the bow back into my hand and said, 'Your great-aunt would like that.' Then he looked down at me with the warm and gentle smile of a man enjoying some secret humour.

Because he was a man who liked to make the most of the little dramas of life he   10
did not tell me immediately of my great-aunt, but chose to be mysterious. I cannot blame him for this. Being postmaster to a small Kentish village offered him little other excitement, and the story of Joshua Tanner and Appearing Day deserved the touch of theatre he gave to it. When he had returned the bow he took one hand from his pocket and gently fingered his watch-fob. 'Come with me, boy,' he said at   15
last. 'I'd like to show you something.'

We walked through the kitchen, through the dusty little post office to the street beyond. He kept his hands in his pockets and walked with great strides that outpaced mine, so that I hopped and skipped along behind him. We went up the street to the Norman church, and when we reached the gate he stopped and   20
played with his watch-fob again, watching me to see how I was responding to the mystery. 'Where would it be, now,' he said, winking slily to let me see that he knew all the time. My curiosity began to generate heat.

'Of course!' he said, and slapped his thigh, 'It's over there, beneath the cypresses.'

So off we went again, across the churchyard, threading our way past the little   25
hummocks of old graves, until we reached a lonely spot, almost overgrown with meadow-sweet and traveller's joy. I looked at it with some disappointment.

My father took a stick and carefully beat down the grass about the grave, and then he scratched the moss from the face of the stone. 'Can you read it?' he asked, looking over his shoulder at me. I could not, and said that I could not, with some   30
truculence, for I had expected more excitement than this. He straightened his back. 'Well then, I shall have to read it for you.' He traced the stick along the inscription on the stone, line by line. 'Here lies…' he said.

Here lies
JOSHUA TANNER   35
of this parish
Late Major of the United States Army
and his beloved wife
APPEARING DAY
a daughter of the Cheyenne, sister of the Arapaho   40
and a devout Christian
Joined in death October 14, 1894
'Nothing lives long, except the earth and the mountains'

When my father had finished reading he repeated the words *a daughter of the Cheyenne, sister of the Arapaho*. There was sadness in his voice, although he was smiling. Then once more he said the words *Cheyenne* and *Arapaho*, and made them sound like notes of some barbaric music. With his hands he gently moved the grass over the grave and threw the stick into the corner of the graveyard. He turned to face me. 'Well, what do you think of that?' 45

What was I to think, except that in this overgrown spot, twenty years before, had been buried two of my distant relatives? I considered this a very poor secret, and the expression on my face must have shown this, for my father's emotions suddenly exploded, blowing his hands out of those tight pockets and flinging them wide from his shoulders. 50

'An Indian, my boy!' he shouted triumphantly, 'A daughter of the Cheyenne. A real Indian buried here in Kent, and she was your great-aunt.' He placed his hand on my shoulder and the wonder of it came to me slowly. When he saw that my imagination was beginning to catch fire he whirled me about and set off smartly across the churchyard, through the creaking gate, down the village street. I trotted behind him, full of questions which were primarily concerned with whether this did or did not make me something of an Indian too. 55 60

From *Spanish Stirrup and Other Stories* by John Prebble

Answer these questions.

1 What would the author's great-aunt have liked?

_____

2 What was his father's job?

_____

3 Where did his father take him?

_____

4 What was the occupation of Joshua Tanner?

_____

5 What are the Cheyenne and the Arapaho?

_____

6 What does 'abruptly' mean (line 6)? _____

7–8 The author says he was 'expecting a rebuke' (lines 6–7). What does this remark tell you about the father and his relationship with his son?

_____

_____

9–10 How can you tell, in the second paragraph, that his father was also rather a kind man?

_____

_____

11–12 The author's father 'liked to make the most of the little dramas of life' (line 10). Explain what this means and why he did this.

_____

_____

13–15 Explain in your own words what the following mean:

a 'touch of theatre' (line 14) (*1 mark*)

_____

'My curiosity began to generate heat.' (*2 marks*)

_____

16 In what year is the author writing?

_____

17–18 Which two **adverbs** does the author use to show that his father treats the grave with respect?

_____

_____

19–20 Name two pieces of evidence in the passage which suggest that the churchyard is not well looked after.

_____

_____

_____

21–22 The author's father experiences two emotions when he reads and says the words 'Cheyenne' and 'Arapaho'. Explain what he feels and why you think he feels like this.

_____

_____

_____

23–24 Explain what the author means when he says: 'my imagination was beginning to catch fire' (lines 57–8).

_____

_____

25–26 How do you know that the author's father likes secrets and mysteries? Give two examples from the passage.

_____

_____

27–28 How do you know that the author was at first unimpressed by what his father showed him? Answer with reference to two parts of the passage.

_____

_____

29–30 Who do you think the watch-fob might have once belonged to? Why?

_____

_____

30

Match each word with its **definition** as used in the passage. Write the correct letter on the answer line.

E 2

31 crude (line 3)	_____	(a) defiance
32 fashioned (line 3)	_____	(b) firstly
33 rebuke (line 7)	_____	(c) small mounds
34 hummocks (line 26)	_____	(d) words on monument
35 truculence (line 31)	_____	(e) fierce/cruel
36 inscription (line 32)	_____	(f) made
37 devout (line 41)	_____	(g) rough/basic
38 barbaric (line 47)	_____	(h) earnestly religious
39 triumphantly (line 55)	_____	(i) telling off
40 primarily (line 60)	_____	(j) exultantly

10

Explain what these **expressions** mean.

41–42 a golden boy

_____

_____

43–44 a half-baked boy

_____

_____

45–46 a mother's boy

_____

_____

47–48 a whipping boy

_____

_____

49–50 the boys in blue

_____

_____

10

E 2

Complete each word with 'le', 'el', or 'al'.

51 eas_____   **52** symmetric_____

53 peop_____   **54** origin_____

55 person_____   **56** mirac_____

57 perpetu_____   **58** satch_____

59 parall_____   **60** vow_____

10

Complete the table.

	Adjective	Adverb	Noun
61–62			curiosity
63–64			disappointment
65–66		abruptly	
67–68		luckily	
69–70	warm		

Complete each **sentence** by choosing the correct word from the brackets.

71 My father (allowed/aloud) _____ me to keep the bow and arrow.

72 Just after my thirteenth birthday he (choose/chose) _____ to tell me about my great-aunt.

73 The inscription was written on the (coarse/course) _____ stone.

74 The (sauce/source) _____ of the mystery was revealed.

75 It was quite a surprise to learn about my (past/passed) _____.

Complete each word with 're' or 'er'.

76 cent_____

77 scann_____

78 centimet_____

79 perimet_____

80 fib_____

81 thermomet_____

82 lit_____

83 gen_____

84 timb_____

85 diamet_____

Use a word or **phrase** to define these.

86 outpace _____

87 outmoded _____

88 outcome _____

89 outwit _____

90 outlay _____

Complete the table.

		+ ing	+ ed
91–92	bury		
93–94	trace		
95–96	quarrel		
97–98	reveal		
99–100	incur		

Now go to the Progress Chart to record your score!   Total

10

100

THE TIMES

TUESDAY SEPTEMBER 26 2006

Harbinger of death in steep decline

By Lewis Smith, Environment Reporter

BARN OWLS, emblematic of the country idyll, have suffered a catastrophic drop in numbers, with up to 75 per cent feared to have been wiped out.

A cold March and a wet May combined 5 to kill off parent birds and create appalling breeding conditions for survivors, the Barn Owl Trust said yesterday. Attempts by the birds to recover by raising late broods were ruined by repeated downpours last month. 10

Fewer than one in four regular breeding sites has been occupied this year in much of the country, and in Shropshire the figure fell to one in twelve.

"It's the worst year ever known," David 15 Ramsden, the head of conservation at the trust, said. He blamed changing weather patterns caused by global warming. "We were very optimistic things were generally picking up but this year has been a huge 20 setback. We aren't just talking about a few less pairs, we are talking about an incredible number less."

Farmers and other barn owners have been so alarmed at the struggle the birds 25 have faced to survive that they have been leaving out food.

Barn owls are harbingers of death in folklore and literature. Shakespeare, Byron, Jonson, Wordsworth and Keats all linked 30 the bird with death or misery.

Now the population has slumped well below the 4,000 pairs recorded in Britain in 1998. It had fallen in England and Wales by 69 per cent from 1932, when 12,142 35 pairs were recorded, to 1985 when 3,778 pairs were surveyed.

Population levels were thought to have stabilised from the 1980s and, since 1998, it was believed that numbers were 40 recovering. But this year's figures have set back conservation efforts by at least a decade.

Mr Ramsden added: "There may be as few as a thousand pairs breeding 45 this year in the whole of the UK. That's catastrophic. The numbers are lower than ten years ago. Almost every year has record-breaking weather and prolonged extreme conditions are bad news for barn 50 owls. The thought that climate change may significantly hinder the recovery of this national treasure is a huge worry to those concerned with barn owl conservation."

Mr Ramsden has been monitoring sites 55 in Devon and collating findings from surveys elsewhere. In Devon only 15 of the 72 regularly monitored nest sites were occupied this year. Most or all would normally be used by the birds and their 60 absence has been repeated in many other countries. A cold March meant that the small mammals on which barn owls prey, particularly voles, were in short supply. Many adults starved to death. The number 65 of dead owls reported in early spring was three times higher than usual.

Persistent rain in May forced the birds to restrict their hunting because the feathers that enable the owl to fly 70 silently get waterlogged easily.

A further sign of an appalling year is the lack of reports this month of owls being struck by vehicles. About 75 per cent of barn owls that die in their first year 75 are killed in this way.

Monitors for the British Trust for Ornithology also reported disastrous results for the owl this year. David Leech, for the BTO, said that the bird had suffered 80

Answer these questions.

1–3 These statistics are used in the newspaper report. To what do they refer?

(a) 'well below 4,000'

_____

(b) '12,142'

_____

(c) '72'

_____

4 How many breeding sites in Shropshire were occupied this year?

_____

5 Were there more or fewer than a thousand breeding pairs of barn owls ten years ago?

_____

6 How many breeding sites in Devon have not been used this year?

_____

7 What does BTO stand for?

_____

8–9 What were the weather conditions like in:

March: _____

May: _____

10–11 How did conditions in these months specifically affect the barn owls?

March: _____

_____

May: _____

_____

12 How can you tell that farmers quite like barn owls?

_____

13 During which decade did barn owl numbers stop going down?

_____

14 Discuss whether the decline of barn owls is unique to Britain.

_____

15–16 In August 2006:

(a) What was the weather like?

_____

(b) How did it affect the barn owls?

_____

17–18 Explain what these **expressions** mean.

(a) 'harbingers of death' (line 28)

_____

(b) 'thought to have stabilised' (lines 38–9)

_____

19 Why do you think it is important for the owls to be able to fly silently?

_____

_____

20–21 How is a 'lack of reports this month of owls being struck by vehicles' a 'further sign of an appalling year'?

_____

_____

22–24 Explain in your own words: 'emblematic of the country idyll' (lines 1–2).

_____

_____

25–27 Find three pieces of evidence in the newspaper report that suggest people care about what happens to barn owls.

_____

_____

_____

28–30 The newspaper reports three sources which confirm the declining number of barn owls. What are they?

(a) _____

(b) _____

(c) _____

30
E 2

Match each word with its **definition** as it is used in the newspaper report.

31	appalling	_____	(a) analysing
32	regular	_____	(b) extended
33	optimistic	_____	(c) continuing
34	incredible	_____	(d) shocking
35	slumped	_____	(e) usual
36	surveyed	_____	(f) hard to believe
37	prolonged	_____	(g) fallen
38	significantly	_____	(h) investigated
39	collating	_____	(i) hopeful
40	persistent	_____	(j) considerably

10
E 2

Complete each **sentence**.

41 Ornithology is the scientific study of _____.

42 Palaeontology is the scientific study of _____.

43 Climatology is the scientific study of _____.

44 Zoology is the scientific study of _____.

45 Pathology is the scientific study of _____.

5
E 2

Complete each word with 'or' or 'ar'.

46 irregul_____   47 auth_____

48 denominat_____   49 supervis_____

50 triangul_____   51 perpendicul_____

52 metaph_____   53 regulat_____

54 muscul_____   55 famili_____

10

D 6

Replace the words in bold with a single **adverb**.

56 Mr Ramsden spoke of the plight of the barn owl **with dejection**.

_____

57 The number of the birds had been counted **with precision**.

_____

58 Rain in May fell **with persistence**.

_____

59 The Trust reported **with optimism** on the number of breeding pairs.

_____

60 'We are unable to improve the situation for the owls,' he said **with candour**.

_____

5

Change these **sentences** from active to passive.

D 1

61 David Ramsden blamed global warming.

_____

62 Extreme weather conditions affect the barn owls.

_____

63 Farmers have left food out for the owls.

_____

64 Monitors reported disastrous results this year.

_____

65 When an owl sees a shrew or a mouse, it drops with talons outspread.

_____

5

Make each **verb** into an **abstract noun** ending in 'tion' or 'sion'.

66 create _____

67 add _____

68 conclude _____

69 invade _____

70 evaluate _____

71 comprehend _____

72 suspend _____

73 celebrate _____

74 solve _____

75 collide _____

10

Explain what these **expressions** mean.

76–77 a bird of ill-omen

_____

_____

78–79 to be able to charm the birds off the trees

_____

_____

80–81 a bird in the hand is worth two in the bush

_____

_____

82–83 to kill two birds with one stone

_____

_____

84–85 birds of a feather flock together

_____

_____

10

In each **sentence**, change the **verb** in bold to a **noun**. Rewrite the **sentences** accordingly.

D 1
D 6

86 Barn owls **prey** on voles.

_____

87 Cold and wet weather **combined** to kill off parent birds.

_____

88 The numbers of pairs **were surveyed** in 1985.

_____

89 The birds **had suffered** particularly badly in the South West.

_____

90 The population **has slumped** alarmingly.

_____

5

Write a **phrase** to explain the meaning of these words.

E 2

91 decade   _____

92 decathlon   _____

93 decagon   _____

94 decapod   _____

95 decahedron   _____

5

Complete each **sentence** with the correct **homophone** from the brackets.

E 2

96 The (practice/practise) _____ of monitoring the birds goes on every year.

97 The extreme weather is the (principle/principal) _____ cause of the declining bird numbers.

98 The small mammals on which barn owls (prey/pray) _____ are in short supply.

99 The owls are (dependant/dependent) _____ on small mammals for their food.

100 We would (counsel/council) _____ all farmers to put out food for the owls in these difficult times.

5

The boy with fair hair lowered himself down the last few feet of rock and began to pick his way towards the lagoon. Though he had taken off his school sweater and trailed it now from one hand, his grey shirt stuck to him and his hair was plastered to his forehead. All round him the long scar smashed into the jungle was a bath of heat. He was clambering heavily among the creepers and broken trunks when a   5
bird, a vision of red and yellow, flashed upwards with a witch-like cry; and this cry was echoed by another.

"Hi!" it said, "wait a minute!"

The undergrowth at the side of the scar was shaken and a multitude of raindrops fell pattering.   10

"Wait a minute," the voice said, "I got caught up."

The fair boy stopped and jerked his stockings with an automatic gesture that made the jungle seem for a moment like the Home Counties.

The voice spoke again.

"I can't hardly move with all these creeper things."   15

The owner of the voice came backing out of the undergrowth so that twigs scratched on a greasy wind-breaker. The naked crooks of his knees were plump, caught and scratched by thorns. He bent down, removed the thorns carefully, and turned round. He was shorter than the fair boy and very fat. He came forward, searching out safe lodgements for his feet, and then looked up through thick spectacles.   20

"Where's the man with the megaphone?"

The fair boy shook his head.

"This is an island. At least I think it's an island. That's a reef out in the sea. Perhaps there aren't any grown-ups anywhere."

The fat boy looked startled.   25

"There was that pilot. But he wasn't in the passenger tube, he was up in the cabin in front."

The fair boy was peering at the reef through screwed-up eyes.

"All them other kids," the fat boy went on. "Some of them must have got out. They must have, mustn't they?"   30

The fair boy began to pick his way as casually as possible towards the water. He tried to be offhand and not too obviously uninterested but the fat boy hurried after him.

"Aren't there any grown-ups at all?"

"I don't think so."

The fair boy said this solemnly; but then the delight of a realized ambition   35
overcame him. In the middle of the scar he stood on his head and grinned at the reversed fat boy.

"No grown-ups!"

The fat boy thought for a moment.

"That pilot."   40

The fair boy allowed his feet to come down and sat on the steamy earth.

"He must have flown off after he dropped us. He couldn't land here. Not in a plane with wheels."

"We was attacked!"

"He'll be back all right."   45

The fat boy shook his head.

"When we was coming down I looked through one of them windows. I saw the other part of the plane. There were flames coming out of it."

He looked up and down the scar.

"And this is what the tube done."

The fair boy reached out and touched the jagged end of a trunk. For a moment he looked interested.

"What happened to it?" he asked. "Where's it got to now?"

"That storm dragged it out to sea. It wasn't half dangerous with all them tree trunks falling. There must have been some kids still in it."

He hesitated for a moment then spoke again.

"What's your name?"

"Ralph."

The fat boy waited to be asked his name in turn but this proffer of acquaintance was not made; the fair boy called Ralph smiled vaguely, stood up, and began to make his way once more towards the lagoon. The fat boy hung steadily at his shoulder.

"I expect there's a lot more of us scattered about. You haven't seen any others have you?"

Ralph shook his head and increased his speed. Then he tripped over a branch and came down with a crash.

The fat boy stood by him, breathing hard.

"My auntie told me not to run," he explained, "on account of my asthma."

"Ass-mar?"

"That's right. Can't catch me breath. I was the only boy in our school what had asthma," said the fat boy with a touch of pride. "And I've been wearing specs since I was three."

From Lord of the Flies by William Golding

Answer these questions.

1 What was the fair-haired boy wearing?

_____

2 How was the boy who came out of the undergrowth different from the fair-haired boy?

_____

3 Which two adults did they think might be on the island?

_____

4 Why does the fat boy think that the plane has been attacked?

_____

_____

5 What **metaphor** does the author use to give the impression of how hot it was?

_____

6 How does the author suggest in the first paragraph that the jungle is a rather sinister place?

_____

7 Explain what the fat boy meant when he said, 'I got caught up' (line 11).

_____

8–9 Find two pieces of evidence in the text which suggest that the weather had been bad.

_____

_____

10 What do you think the 'passenger tube' was?

_____

11–12 What was the 'realized ambition' (line 35) that came over Ralph?

_____

_____

13–14 How do you know that it was difficult for Ralph to move towards the lagoon? Give two examples to explain your answer.

_____

_____

15–16 How do you know that:

    (a)   the fat boy was uncomfortable at the thought of no adults on the island?

    _____

    (b)   Ralph was pleased that there were no adults on the island?

    _____

17–19 Give three reasons why the fat boy thinks that the pilot won't be coming back.

_____

_____

_____

20–22 (a)   Which of the boys is anxious to know if there are any other survivors? (_1 mark_)

    _____

(b) Give two examples from the passage to explain your answer. (*2 marks*)

_____

_____

23–24 Explain in your own words what 'this proffer of acquaintance' (line 59) means.

_____

25–27 How do you know that Ralph is not interested in being friends with the fat boy? Give examples from the text to explain your answer.

_____

_____

28–30 Describe the personality of the fat boy in your own words.

_____

_____

30

Match each word with its **definition** as used in the passage.

E 2

31 multitude	_____	(a) offer
32 automatic	_____	(b) seriously
33 lodgements	_____	(c) without thinking
34 solemnly	_____	(d) safe places
35 proffer	_____	(e) a great many

5

Complete the **verb** table.

D 6

	he flies	he flew	he has flown
36	he draws		
37	he goes		
38	he writes		
39	he swims		
40	he grows		
41	he comes		
42	he drives		
43	he gives		
44	he is		
45	he speaks		

10

Complete each word with 'ance' or 'ence'.

46 resembl_____ **47** entr_____

48 evid_____ **49** conveni_____

50 perform_____ **51** abs_____

52 repugn_____ **53** audi_____

54 resist_____ **55** obedi_____

E 2

10

Explain what these **expressions** mean.

56–57 to pour oil on troubled waters

_____

58–59 to pour cold water on something

_____

60–61 to be dull as ditchwater

_____

62–63 to be in hot water

_____

64–65 water under the bridge

_____

10

E 2

Solve the clues with 'ph' words.

66 funnel-shaped hand-held device for making the voice louder _____

67 a musical instrument _____

68 a fear of open spaces _____

69 a comparison where something is said to be something else _____

70 a terrible disaster _____

5

Write these **sentences** correctly.

D 1

71 'We was attacked!'

_____

72–73 'When we was coming down I looked through one of them windows.'

_____

74 'Can't catch me breath.'

_____

75 'I was the only boy in our school what had asthma.'

_____

5

Add 'a', 'ai', 'ei' or 'ay' to complete each word.

E 2

76 w_____ght   **77** str_____ght

78 persu_____de   **79** all_____

80 oct_____ve   **81** r_____gn

82 cont_____n   **83** sl_____gh

84 del_____   **85** st_____d

10

Write V (**verb**) or A (**adjective**) for each word in bold.

D 6

86 The **dripping** raindrops pattered around him. _____

87 The raindrops were **dripping** from the trees. _____

88 The **squawking** bird flew overhead. _____

89 **Squawking** noisily, the bird flew away. _____

90 Ralph was **grinning** as he stood on his head. _____

91 The **grinning** boy stood on his head. _____

6

Write **antonyms** for these words.

92 increased _____

93 lowered _____

94 heavily _____

95 uninterested _____

96 dangerous _____

97 vaguely _____

98 spacious _____

99 stingy _____

100 logical _____

9

Now go to the Progress Chart to record your score!   Total   100

Paper 4

Howard Carter was an archaeologist who excavated in the Valley of the Kings in Egypt. This is an extract from his autobiography when he discovered the tomb of Tutankhamen in 1922.

This was to be our final season in The Valley. Six full seasons we had excavated there, and season after season had drawn a blank; we had worked for months at a stretch and found nothing, and only an excavator knows how desperately depressing that can be; we had almost made up our minds that we were beaten, and were preparing to leave The Valley and try our luck elsewhere; and then 5 – hardly had we set hoe to ground in our last despairing effort than we made a discovery that far exceeded our wildest dreams. Surely, never before in the whole history of excavation has a full digging season been compressed within the space of five days.

Let me try and tell the story of it all. It will not be easy, for the dramatic 10 suddenness of the initial discovery left me in a dazed condition, and the months that have followed have been so crowded with incident that I have hardly had time to think. Setting it down on paper will perhaps give me a chance to realize what has happened and all that it means.

I arrived in Luxor on October 28th, and by November 1st I had enrolled my
workmen and was ready to begin. Our former excavations had stopped short
at the north-east corner of the tomb of Rameses VI, and from this point I started
trenching southwards. It will be remembered that in this area there were a number
of roughly constructed workmen's huts, used probably by the labourers in the tomb
of Rameses… After we had planned and noted them, they were removed, and we   *20*
were ready to clear away the three feet of soil that lay beneath them.

Hardly had I arrived on the work the next morning (November 4th) than the
unusual silence, due to the stoppage of work, made me realize that something out
of the ordinary had happened, and I was greeted by the announcement that a steep
cut in the rock had been discovered underneath the very first hut to be attacked.   *25*
This seemed too good to be true, but a short amount of extra clearing revealed the
fact that we were actually in the entrance of a steep cut in the rock, some thirteen
feet below the entrance to the tomb of Rameses VI, and a similar depth from the
present bed level of The Valley. The manner of cutting was that of a sunken stairway
entrance so common in The Valley, and I almost dared to hope that we had   *30*
found our tomb at last. Work continued feverishly throughout the whole of that day
and the morning of the next, but it was not until the afternoon of November 5th that
we succeeded in clearing away the masses of rubbish that overlay the cut, and
were able to demarcate the upper edges of the stairway on all four sides.

It was clear by now beyond any question that we actually had before us the   *35*
entrance to a tomb, but doubts, born of previous disappointments, persisted in
creeping in. There was always the horrible possibility, suggested by our experience
in the Thothmes III Valley, that the tomb was an unfinished one, never completed
and never used: if it had been finished there was the depressing possibility that it
had been completely plundered in ancient times. On the other hand, there was just   *40*
the chance of an untouched or only partially plundered tomb, and it was with ill-
suppressed excitement that I watched the descending steps of the staircase, as one
by one they came to light. The cutting was excavated in the side of a small hillock,
and, as the work progressed, its western edge receded under the slope of the rock
until it was, first partially, and then completely, roofed in, and became a passage,   *45*
10 feet high by 6 feet wide. Work progressed more rapidly now; step succeeded
step, and at the level of the twelfth, towards sunset, there was disclosed the upper
part of a doorway, blocked, plastered and sealed.

A sealed doorway – it was actually true, then! Our years of patient labour were to
be rewarded after all, and I think my first feeling was one of congratulation that my   *50*
faith in The Valley had not been unjustified.

From *The Discovery of the Tomb of Tutankhamen* by Howard Carter and A C Mace

Answer these questions.

Write T (true) or F (false) against each statement.

1 Carter had been excavating in the Valley of the Kings for six seasons. _____

2 Carter arrived in Luxor on November 1st. _____

3 The area Carter was interested in was covered with workmen's huts. _____

4 A steep cut into the rock was discovered under the third hut to be cleared away. _____

5 The discovered tomb had been completely plundered in ancient times. _____

6 A 'season' in the Valley of the Kings ran from October to March. Why do you think Carter only worked during these months?

_____

7 What was special about Carter's digging season?

_____

_____

8–11 Explain what these **expressions** mean.

drawn a blank _____

out of the ordinary _____

too good to be true _____

beyond any question _____

12 How did the workmen's huts hamper Carter's work?

_____

_____

13 How do you know that the excavation site was usually noisy and busy?

_____

_____

14 How many steps did the workmen uncover? _____

15–16 Where had Carter excavated before and why had it been a disappointing experience?

_____

_____

17–20 What do these words mean?

'demarcate' (line 34) _____

'ill-suppressed' (lines 41–2) _____

'trenching' (line 18) _____

'persisted' (line 36) _____

21–22 Describe how Carter was feeling at the beginning of the extract. Quote from the extract to support your answer.

_____

_____

23–24 Write in your own words what Carter hoped to achieve by writing about his find.

_____

_____

25–26 Explain in your own words the two main reasons why Carter wrote 'it will not be easy' to tell the story of the discovery.

_____

_____

27–28 Why do you think Carter uses the word 'feverishly' to describe the work after the first step had been uncovered?

_____

_____

29–30 Carter was sure he had found the entrance to a tomb but 'doubts … persisted in creeping in'. Explain in your own words why he had doubts and what they were.

_____

_____

31 How can you tell that, although Carter had doubts, he was still optimistic?

_____

_____

32 What was the sure sign that a tomb had not been plundered?

_____

33 What time of day did Carter realise that the tomb had not been robbed?

_____

34–35 Explain in your own words what Carter's main emotions were when he discovered the sealed doorway.

_____

_____

35

Write the **synonym** for each word as it is used in the extract. Begin with the given initial letter.

D 9

36	constructed	b_____
37	labourers	w_____
38	revealed	s_____
39	faith	b_____
40	endeavoured	t_____
41	compressed	s_____
42	enrolled	h_____
43	plundered	r_____
44	former	p_____
45	feverishly	f_____

10

Complete the table.

E 2

	Adjective	Comparative	Superlative
46	wild		
47	rough		
48	dramatic		
49	unusual		
50	gloomy		
51	good		
52	bad		
53	low		

8

Explain what these **expressions** mean.

54–55 to discuss something behind closed doors

_____

56–57 to show someone the door

_____

58–59 to let something in through the back door

_____

60–61 to lay something at someone's door

_____

62–63 to lock the stable door after the horse has bolted

_____

10

The missing letter or letters in these words make the sound 'sh'. Add: 't', 's', 'ch', 'ss' or 'ci' to complete each word.

E 2

64 loca_____ion

65 vi_____ion

66 excur_____ion

67 vaca_____ion

68 pa_____ion

69 edi_____ion

70 omi_____ion

71 profi_____ent

72 _____auffeur

73 interroga_____ion

10

Write the **diminutive** of each word.

D 8

74 hill _____

75 book _____

76 note _____

77 statue _____

78 grain _____

5

Write whether each word in bold is an **adjective**, **adverb** or a **noun**.

79 The **danger** of running out of money was very real. _____

80 Carter was **dangerously** close to running out of money.

_____

81 Carter found himself in a **dangerous** situation. _____

82 They removed the huts **carefully**. _____

83 The **careful** workmen removed the huts. _____

84 The workmen removed the huts with **care**. _____

85 Carter said the measurements must be **exact**. _____

86 They measured the uncovered step **exactly**. _____

87 The **exactness** of the measurement was important. _____

88 What they found in the tomb was **magnificent**. _____

89 Some of the objects were **magnificently** decorated. _____

90 The **magnificence** of the tomb astonished Carter. _____

Complete each word with 'ent' or 'ant'.

91 depend_____   **92** instrum_____

93 transpar_____   **94** hesit_____

95 perman_____   **96** irrelev_____

97 defici_____   **98** stagn_____

99 leni_____   **100** poign_____

Paper 5

Many famous stories have their origins in the mists of time. They tell of brave heroes, daring deeds, unspeakable monsters and impossible quests. One such story is Theseus and the Minotaur.

According to legend, there lived, under the magnificent palace in Crete, a monster known as the Minotaur. This fearsome creature had the body of a huge man and the head of a bull. Its rapacious appetite could only be sated by human flesh and his thirst slaked by human blood. King Minos of Crete satisfied the monster with youths and maidens from the lands he conquered. 5

When King Aegeus was in the unhappy position of sending human sacrifices to appease the ravening monster, his son, Theseus, stated his intention to be one of the victims. He declared that he would slay the beast or share the fate of his countrymen and women. 10

Aegeus trembled with foreboding. He did not want his son to go but Theseus was adamant. 'If I conquer the Minotaur,' he said, 'never again will our people have to meet this horrifying fate.' 15

In the face of his son's determination, Aegeus had no option but to agree. He was proud of his son's bravery and buried his fear deep in his heart. 'The ship you will voyage in to death or glory will bear black sails. Should you be victorious in your quest, hoist white sails on your return so we can prepare the celebrations. If the ship returns to our harbour with sails unchanged, we will know that all have perished in the labyrinthine tomb.' 20

Theseus promised this and knelt before him for his blessing. Their formal farewell belied the depth of their sorrow at parting in this way.

A melancholy voyage brought Theseus and the other victims to the shores of Crete. They were escorted with ceremony to the palace which was to be their prison, where fate intervened in the form of Ariadne, daughter of King Minos. Seeing Theseus' bravery and regal bearing, she fell immediately in love with him and determined to save him or die in the attempt. 25

In the dead of night, Ariadne stole through the cavernous halls of the palace to where Theseus was imprisoned. 'You must follow my instructions exactly,' she whispered to him. 'At daybreak, you will be escorted to the Labyrinth. Make sure you are the first to enter. Conceal this ball of thread about your person. When the door of the Labyrinth is closed on you, tie one end to the door. Unroll it as you go so it will serve as a means of escape. I will conceal myself near the entrance and let you out should you prevail.' 30

Theseus felt a dim flickering of optimism as he listened intently to her words. The echoing sound of footsteps startled them both. 'It is the guard,' Theseus hissed. 'You must leave!' 35

'I will, but you must make me a promise. Swear on the life we are trying to preserve!'

'Anything,' Theseus whispered fervently, 'but hurry.' 40

'If you survive the ordeal the gods have decreed you must face, you must ensure my survival. If ever my father discovered I had aided you to defeat the Minotaur, my life would be forfeit.'

'You will be on my ship and safe before our plan is discovered,' he assured her. 'Now go!' 45

Sleep eluded Theseus that night and, at the first paling of the eastern sky, he found himself alone in the Labyrinth. The chill of the rough, stone walls seeped into his bones and he felt a thin film of sweat on his skin. The blood pounded in his ears. He secured the thread and began the tortuous journey to the centre of the maze. A low, blood-curdling growl from the monster guided Theseus to its lair. Nothing had prepared him for the sight he encountered which made the very blood freeze in his veins and, momentarily, robbed him of his wits. The Minotaur fell silent. Man and monster locked eyes. Then, with speed belying its huge bulk, the monster flung himself at Theseus. 50

He regained his wits in time to land a forceful punch on the monster's heart. 55 He leapt aside and when the monster attacked again, he repeated the blow. Over and over, Theseus pounded until the Minotaur was visibly weakened. He then seized his opportunity as the monster staggered in pain and anger. With a defiant shout, Theseus leapt on to the Minotaur's back, grabbed its hideous horns and, summoning the last of his strength, wrenched the creature's head back. The 60 sickening crack of its breaking neck echoed through the maze. Theseus leapt aside as the gargantuan body smashed to the ground.

Theseus stood, looking at the dead monster with horror and fascination until some ethereal voice in his head urged him to flee. The living nightmare was not yet over.

He pressed his body to the wall and edged towards the opening. Once outside 65 the Minotaur's tomb, he began to think clearly. He fumbled for the thread and retraced his steps. Flinging himself on the door, he pounded with what remained of his strength.

Ariadne was true to her word. Wrenching open the door, she dragged Theseus from the realms of death into the warmth of the sunlight. 70

Answer these questions.

1 What was the colour of the sails of the boat which took Theseus to Crete?

_____

2 Where did Minos rule?

_____

3 What promise did Theseus make to Ariadne?

_____

4 What time of day did Theseus enter the Labyrinth?

_____

5 What did the Minotaur look like?

_____

6–7 How did Aegeus feel when Theseus said he wanted to go to Crete to fight the Minotaur?

_____

_____

8–9 Explain in your own words why Ariadne fell in love with Theseus. Give two reasons.

_____

_____

10 Why do you think Ariadne instructed Theseus to go into the Labyrinth first?

_____

_____

11–12 In what two ways could Theseus meet his death?

_____

_____

13–14 What was Ariadne frightened about?

_____

_____

15 Underline the word you think best describes Ariadne.

romantic   resourceful   slow-witted

16–17 Find two pieces of evidence from the passage to support your answer above.

_____

_____

18 Underline the word you think best describes Theseus.

cowardly   stupid   valiant

19–20 Find two pieces of evidence from the passage to support your answer above.

_____

_____

21–23 Explain in your own words the three stages by which Theseus weakened and killed the Minotaur.

_____

_____

_____

23

E 2

Circle the **definition** which is closest in meaning to the word in bold as it is used in the passage.

24 hoist	put up	buy	make
25 blow	insult	punch	waft
26 labyrinth	palace	race	maze
27 prevail	suffer	win	lose
28 flee	escape	wandering	walk
29 blessing	gift	support	speech
30 intention	fear	luck	proposal
31 stole	moved stealthily	took unlawfully	crawled

8

D 9

Find **antonyms** in the passage for these words.

32 defeated _____

33 survived _____

34 ashamed _____

35 concealed _____

36 cowardice _____

5

D 6

E 2

Write these as **adjectives** which end in the **suffix** 'some'.

37 inclined to argue _____

38 daring, inclined to take risks _____

39 pure, natural _____

40 causing fear _____

41 tedious and irritating _____

5

Some questions will be answered in the children's own words. Answers to these questions are given in *italics*. Any answers that seem to be in line with these should be marked correct.

Paper 1

1. the bow and arrow
2. postmaster
3. to the churchyard
4. Major in the United States army
5. Native American (Indian) tribes
6. *suddenly*
7–8. *that because the father was rather strict, it was common for the boy to be told off*
9–10. He had a warm and gentle smile.
11–12. *He liked to make the small events of everyday life exciting. He did this because his job was dull.*
13–15. *a bit of dramatic excitement; my interest started to make me excited*
16. 1914
17–18. '**carefully** beat down the grass'
      '**gently** moved the grass over the grave'
19–20. *'almost overgrown with meadow-sweet and traveller's joy'; 'beat down the grass'; 'overgrown spot'; 'the creaking gate'*
21–22. *sadness because his relatives are dead; triumph because he and his son are related to the Cheyenne and the Arapaho*
23–24. *It was beginning to dawn on the author that he was related to an Indian and that this was an exciting prospect.*
25–26. *He didn't immediately tell his son about his great-aunt. He says, 'I'd like to show you something' but he does not say what. He pretended that he could not remember where the grave was. He says, 'Where would it be, now'.*
27–28. *The author showed disappointment. He says, 'with some disappointment'; 'I had expected more excitement than this'; 'a very poor secret'.*
29–30. *The watch-fob possibly once belonged to Joshua Tanner. The author's father 'fingered his watch-fob' as he thought about telling his son about Great-Aunt Appearing Day. He 'played with his watch-fob again' when they reached the churchyard gate.*
31. (g) rough/basic
32. (f) made
33. (i) telling off
34. (c) small mounds
35. (a) defiance
36. (d) words on monument
37. (h) earnestly religious
38. (e) fierce/cruel
39. (j) exultantly
40. (b) firstly
41–42. *a young man who is idolised for his good looks or skill*
43–44. *a foolish or stupid boy*
45–46. *a boy who is indulged or spoilt by his mother*

47–48. *someone who is made responsible for the mistakes or faults of others*
49–50. the police
51. easel
52. symmetrical
53. people
54. original
55. personal
56. miracle
57. perpetual
58. satchel
59. parallel
60. vowel

	Adjective	Adverb	Noun
61–62	curious	curiously	curiosity
63–64	disappointing	disappointedly	disappointment
65–66	abrupt	abruptly	abruptness
67–68	lucky	luckily	luck
69–70	warm	warmly	warmth

71. allowed
72. chose
73. coarse
74. source
75. past
76. centre
77. scanner
78. centimetre
79. perimeter
80. fibre
81. thermometer
82. litre
83. genre
84. timber/timbre
85. diameter
86. *walk faster than*
87. *old-fashioned*
88. *end result*
89. *get the better of*
90. *expenditure*

		+ ing	+ ed
91–92	bury	burying	buried
93–94	trace	tracing	traced
95–96	quarrel	quarrelling	quarrelled
97–98	reveal	revealing	revealed
99–100	incur	incurring	incurred

1 pairs of barn owls recorded in England and Wales in 1998
2 pairs of barn owls recorded in England and Wales in 1932
3 regularly monitored nest sites occupied by barn owls in Devon
4 one in twelve
5 more
6 57
7 British Trust for Ornithology
8–9 March – cold
   May – wet
10–11 *March: 'small mammals on which barn owls prey… were in short supply. Many adults starved to death.' May: 'Persistent rain… forced the birds to restrict their hunting because the feathers that enable the owl to fly silently get waterlogged easily.'*
12 *The farmers have been putting out food for them.*
13 *the 1980s*
14 *No, their absence has been repeated in many other countries.*
15–16 *(a) very wet: reference to 'repeated downpours'*
   (b) ruined attempts to raise late broods
17–18 *(a) something that signals the coming of death to whoever sees it*
   (b) believed to have stayed at the same level
19 *to catch prey without any warning of their approach*
20–21 *Fewer reports mean fewer owls of under one year.*
22–24 *symbolises the idea of a perfect existence in the countryside*
25–27 [Any three from] farmers and barn owners put out food; the barn owl is referred to as a 'national treasure'; Mr Ramsden says that the level of breeding pairs is 'catastrophic'; it is a huge worry to those concerned with barn owl conservation; existence of an official group – the Barn Owl Trust
28–30 the Barn Owl Trust; the British Trust for Ornithology; surveys in 'many other countries'
31 (d) shocking
32 (e) usual
33 (i) hopeful
34 (f) hard to believe
35 (g) fallen
36 (h) investigated
37 (b) extended
38 (j) considerably
39 (a) analysing
40 (c) continuing
41 birds
42 fossils
43 climate
44 animals
45 disease
46 irregular
47 author
48 denominator
49 supervisor
50 triangular
51 perpendicular
52 metaphor
53 regulator
54 muscular
55 familiar
56 dejectedly
57 precisely
58 persistently
59 optimistically
60 candidly
61 Global warming was blamed by David Ramsden.
62 The barn owls are affected by extreme weather conditions.
63 Food has been left out by farmers for the owls.
64 Disastrous results were reported by monitors this year.
65 When a shrew or mouse is seen by an owl, the owl drops with talons outspread.
66 creation
67 addition
68 conclusion
69 invasion
70 evaluation
71 comprehension
72 suspension
73 celebration
74 solution
75 collision
76–77 *someone or something that brings bad luck*
78–79 *to have so much charm one can achieve anything with it*
80–81 *a smaller advantage now is better than a possibility of a greater one sometime in the future*
82–83 *to achieve two results by taking one action*
84–85 *people who are of a similar character often become friends*
86 *Voles are the prey of barn owls.*
87 *A combination of cold and wet weather has killed off parent birds.*
88 *In 1985, a survey was taken of the number of pairs.*
89 *The suffering of the birds was particularly bad in the South West.*
90 *The slump in the population is alarming.*
91 *period of ten years*
92 *athletic competition with ten events*
93 *flat shape with ten sides and ten angles*
94 *crustacean with five pairs of walking legs*
95 *solid figure with ten faces*
96 practice
97 principal
98 prey
99 dependent
100 counsel

Paper 3

1 *school sweater; grey shirt/school uniform; stockings*
2 *he was shorter/very fat*
3 the man with the megaphone; the pilot
4 *he saw flames coming from the plane*
5 'bath of heat'
6 *the witch-like cry of the bird*
7 *He got tangled in the undergrowth.*
8–9 *'a multitude of raindrops fell pattering'; 'That storm dragged it out to sea'*
10 *a chute through which passengers could escape from a damaged plane*
11–12 *He had wanted to be in a world which was not controlled by adults and now he found that was the case.*
13–14 *[Any two from] 'pick his way'; 'clambering heavily'; 'tripped over a branch'*
15–16 *(a) [either of] 'looked startled'; asked 'Aren't there any grown-ups at all?'*
(b) [either of] 'stood on his head'; 'grinned at the fat boy'
17–19 *He thinks they were attacked. He saw that the plane was on fire. The pilot didn't stay to help them.*
20–22 (a) the fat boy
(b) *[any two from] 'All them other kids'; 'Some of them must have got out'; 'I expect there's a lot more of us scattered about'*
23–24 *an offer of friendship*
25–27 *He seems anxious to get away from him. [Any from] 'The fair boy began to pick his way as casually as possible'; 'increased his speed'; he does not ask the name of the fat boy.*
28–30 *[Any from] anxious; timid; fearful; friendly; proud of his asthma*
31 (e) a great many
32 (c) without thinking
33 (d) safe places
34 (b) seriously
35 (a) offer

	he flies	he flew	he has flown
36	he draws	he drew	he has drawn
37	he goes	he went	he has been
38	he writes	he wrote	he has written
39	he swims	he swam	he has swum
40	he grows	he grew	he has grown
41	he comes	he came	he has come
42	he drives	he drove	he has driven
43	he gives	he gave	he has given
44	he is	he was	he has been
45	he speaks	he spoke	he has spoken

46 resemblance
47 entrance
48 evidence
49 convenience
50 performance
51 absence
52 repugnance
53 audience
54 resistance
55 obedience
56–57 *to help resolve an argument by being tactful or fair*
58–59 *to find fault with*
60–61 *to be uninteresting/boring*
62–63 *to be in trouble*
64–65 *things that are now in the past and cannot be changed*
66 megaphone
67 *saxophone/xylophone*
68 agoraphobia
69 metaphor
70 catastrophe
71 'We were attacked!'
72–73 'When we were coming down I looked through one of those windows.'
74 'Can't catch my breath.'
75 'I was the only boy in our school who had asthma.'
76 weight
77 straight
78 persuade
79 allay
80 octave
81 reign
82 contain
83 sleigh
84 delay
85 staid
86 A
87 V
88 A
89 V
90 V
91 A
92 decreased
93 raised
94 lightly
95 interested
96 safe
97 precisely/clearly
98 cramped/small
99 generous/kind
100 illogical

Paper 4

1	T	2	F
3	T	4	F
5	F		

6 *From April to September it would be too hot to work in the desert.*
7 *It only lasted five days.*
8–11 come up with nothing/discovered nothing; unusual; unbelievable; certainly
12 *They were built over the site which Carter wanted to excavate.*
13 *Carter refers to an 'unusual silence' which he puts down to the 'stoppage of work' indicating he was used to the noise of the workmen on a busy site.*

14 twelve

15–16 *He had excavated in the Thothmes III Valley. It had been disappointing because they had found a tomb but it had never been finished or used.*

17–20 *mark out; something one tries to hide without success; digging trenches; continued*

21–22 *Carter was depressed/felt that he had failed. [Any from] 'found nothing'; 'desperately depressing'; 'we were beaten'; 'try our luck elsewhere'; 'last despairing effort'*

23–24 *He hoped to understand what had happened and what it meant.*

25–26 *because he was dazed by his discovery and had been so busy that he had not had time to think*

27–28 *to convey the impression of haste and excitement; Carter and his workmen were desperate to find the entrance to the tomb*

29–30 *He had doubts because of previous disappointments in the Thothmes Valley. He wondered if the tomb had never been finished, or if it had been robbed.*

31 *Carter admits to 'ill-suppressed excitement' which shows he still hoped he had made a great discovery.*

32 it was blocked, plastered and sealed

33 towards sunset

34–35 *a sense that he had been proved right; he felt proud of himself for having the courage of his convictions*

36 built
37 workmen
38 showed
39 belief
40 tried
41 shortened
42 hired
43 robbed
44 previous
45 frantically

	Adjective	Comparative	Superlative
46	wild	wilder	wildest
47	rough	rougher	roughest
48	dramatic	more dramatic	most dramatic
49	unusual	more unusual	most unusual
50	gloomy	gloomier	gloomiest
51	good	better	best
52	bad	worse	worst
53	low	lower	lowest

54–55 *to discuss something in complete privacy or secrecy*

56–57 *to request someone to leave*

58–59 *to introduce something into a situation without other people noticing*

60–61 *to blame someone for something that has gone disastrously wrong*

62–63 *to do something after an event has occurred instead of before*

64 location
65 vision
66 excursion
67 vacation
68 passion
69 edition
70 omission
71 proficient
72 chauffeur
73 interrogation
74 hillock
75 booklet
76 notelet
77 statuette
78 granule
79 noun
80 adverb
81 adjective
82 adverb
83 adjective
84 noun
85 adjective
86 adverb
87 noun
88 adjective
89 adverb
90 noun
91 dependant/dependent
92 instrument
93 transparent
94 hesitant
95 permanent
96 irrelevant
97 deficient
98 stagnant
99 lenient
100 poignant

Paper 5

1 black
2 Crete
3 *that he would take her home on his ship*
4 *at dawn*
5 *he had the body of a huge man and the head of a bull*
6–7 *he felt fearful/sorrowful but also proud*
8–9 *because of his courage and his royal manner; 'regal bearing'*
10 *if he succeeded, he would save the lives of the other youths and maidens*
11–12 he could be killed and eaten by the Minotaur; he could be lost forever in the Labyrinth
13–14 *that Theseus would be killed; that she would be killed if her father found out that she had been helping Theseus*
15 resourceful
16–17 *[Any two from] she thought of the plan which allowed Theseus to get out of the Labyrinth; she ensured that he went in first; she hid herself near the entrance to let him out; she had realised her own danger and made sure that Theseus would ensure her safety*
18 valiant
19–20 *he volunteered to go with the others to Crete to face the Minotaur; he killed the Minotaur without a weapon*
21–23 *Theseus killed the Minotaur by hitting it repeatedly on the heart to weaken it; grabbing the creature by the horns; breaking its neck.*
24 put up
25 punch
26 maze
27 win
28 escape
29 support
30 proposal
31 moved stealthily
32 victorious
33 perished
34 proud
35 discovered
36 bravery
37 quarrelsome
38 adventuresome
39 wholesome
40 fearsome
41 tiresome
42 voice
43 tabloid
44 oyster
45 employment

46 moisture
47 decoy
48 boycott
49 alloy
50 exploit
51 embroil
52–53 Theseus thought he would need a helmet, a shield, a net and a sword to defeat the Minotaur.
54–55 'You must do as I tell you,' said Ariadne, 'and you will succeed.'
56–57 The Labyrinth, built by Minos, was the home of the Minotaur.
58 Theseus broke the Minotaur's neck, killing it instantly.
59 The other victims made their way to the ship, crept quietly aboard and sailed away.
60 miserable
61 painful
62 monstrous
63 hungry
64 doomed
65–66 *to supervise someone very closely*
67–68 *to be severely punished*
69–70 *to predict something which could turn out to be wrong*
71–72 *to be absolutely level/even*
73–74 *to be deeply involved in something*
75 school
76 schooner
77 schedule
78 scheme
79 scholar

	Adjective	Adverb	Noun
80–81	bold	boldly	boldness
82–83	violent	violently	violence
84–85	brave	bravely	bravery
86–87	wicked	wickedly	wickedness
88–89	prudent	prudently	prudence

90 dew
91 caught
92 grate
93 canvass
94 manor
95 beet
96 Theseus, who was the son of Aegeus, lived in Athens.
97 They sailed in a ship which had black sails.
98 Ariadne, who fell in love with Theseus, decided to help him.
99 She gave Theseus a ball of thread with which he could find his way out of the Labyrinth.
100 Theseus saw the Minotaur who was bellowing with rage.

1 in the crumbling wall which surrounded the garden
2 *He did not have a chance to take the scorpions up to his bedroom.*
3 Larry's
4 'like confetti'
5 a railway engine
6 *He suggested they should be hit with a book.*
7–8 *she was agitated; she was annoyed at being shut up in the matchbox*
9 *'Every matchbox in the house is a deathtrap'*
10–11 *[Any two from] 'Lugaretzia was the only stranger in the room'; Roger bit her because he thought the family was under attack; her unusual-sounding name*
12–14 *(a) the incorrect thought; (b) an unsuccessful try; (c) hidden*
15 *'I spent half an hour'; they had to be 'rounded up'*
16 *He knew that the rest of family were very cross with him.*
17–19 *It tells you that he was interested in, and fond of, the scorpions: he carefully collected all the babies; it took him some time to do it; the reluctance with which he let them go; his concern to return them to the place from which they had come*
20–21 *fascinated/entranced by*
ran about/covered everything in a mass
22–24 *[any from] he was 'enraptured' by the scorpion family; he wanted to see them grow up; he fed Roger 'surreptitiously'; he made 'impassioned pleas' to save the scorpions*
25–26 *The impression is that the family were all speaking at once. There was general confusion and no one was listening to anyone else.*
27 (c) secretly
28 (h) unaware
29 (f) speed
30 (a) unlucky
31 (d) puzzled
32 (e) confusion
33 (i) begging
34 (g) dismissed
35 (b) wise
36 knight
37 wrap
38 wretch
39 knew
40 plumb
41 scent
42 wring
43 write
44 The family were having lunch.
45 He had been collecting insects for many years.
46 The family would have liked a peaceful meal.
47 The scorpion might have been killed.
48 He will hide his matchboxes in the future.
49 disclosure
50 temperature
51 leisure
52 infrastructure
53 architecture

54 caricature
55 composure
56 manufacture
57 censure
58 moisture
59–60 *to harm the person on whom you depend for a living*
61–62 *to cooperate closely with someone*
63–64 *to have someone in your power*
65–66 *to be good at doing something*
67–68 *to have it under control*
69 them
70 him
71 It
72 her
73 their
74 desperation
75 completion
76 promptness
77 hysteria
78 generosity
79 withdraw a claim/withdraw from an argument
80 support/help
81 retreat from a situation
82 withdraw from an agreement/leave backwards
83 slander
84 unfriendliness
85 distressful/distressing/distressed
86 returning/returned/upturned
87 inaccurately
88 extraordinarily
89 immoveable/unmoving/unmoved
90 like
91 as
92 as
93 as
94 As
95 verb
96 noun
97 adjective
98 noun
99 verb
100 adjective

Paper 7

1 winter
2 *The poet writes 'I leant upon a coppice gate' indicating he is alone and that 'all mankind that haunted nigh/Had sought their household fires' which suggests everyone else is at home.*
3 *the rhythm of the earth and the germination of seeds and the growth of plants, trees, crops etc.*
4 *the song of a thrush*
5 *[Any two from] aged/frail/gaunt/small*
6 *far away or nearby*
7–8 *dusk/evening; 'The weakening eye of day'/In a full-hearted evensong/His happy good-night air*
9–10 *(a) ghost-like; (b) feathers ruffled by the wind*
11–12 *dispirited/lacking energy and enthusiasm*
13–14 *He saw nothing in his surroundings that could be the cause of such 'ecstatic sound'.*
15–16 *The bird must have known that there was something worth singing about: 'Some blessed Hope, whereof he knew And I was unaware.'*

17–19 *'Century's corpse'; 'his crypt'; 'his death-lament'*
20 *'Like strings of broken lyres'*
21–22 *the similarity between the two, e.g. bine-stems and lyre strings are thin; broken lyre strings would stick out at angles like the bine-stems*
23–25 *[Any three from] 'spectre-grey'; 'dregs'; 'desolate'; 'shrunken hard and dry'*
26–28 *[Any three from] 'full-hearted evensong'; 'joy-illimited'; 'fling his soul'; 'ecstatic sound'; 'happy goodnight air'*
29 analyse
30 audience
31 decision
32 evidence
33 necessary
34 sincerely
35 perspective
36 recipe
37 citizen
38 sensor
39–40 *to act in a way that is very close to being illegal*
41–42 *to get an early warning that something is going to happen*
43–44 *to regain energy and enthusiasm*
45–46 *to talk to someone without getting a reasonable response*
47–48 *to anticipate what someone is going to do or say and to do or say it first*
49 I walked over the fields in the early evening.
50 The wind whistled through the trees with a low moan.
51 I saw a thrush sitting on the highest branch.
52 The bird sang loudly and joyfully.
53 It began to snow so I walked back in a hurry.
54 world-famous
55 mid-eighties
56 strange-looking
57 best-known
58 far-fetched
59 physical
60 acrylic
61 brief
62 dynasty
63 hygiene
64 polyester
65 vitamin
66 myth
67 rhyme
68 dynamics
69 (c) group of small trees
70 (a) barren
71 (e) musical instruments
72 (b) thin and haggard
73 (d) of the earth
74 clear
75 meagre
76 doleful
77 sturdy
78 destitute
79 illegal
80 immature
81 unnatural
82 innumerable
83 irregular
84 immoral
85 illegible
86 irrational
87 immobile
88 illogical
89 We leant upon coppice gates.
90 They were unhappy and lonely in the fields.
91 The birds sang their songs from high in the trees.
92 The poets do not know why the birds are singing so ecstatically.
93 advice
94 advise
95 license
96 licence
97 practise
98 practice
99 prophecy
100 prophesy

Paper 8

1 nearly midnight
2 good; faithful
3 flock
4 the lower meadow
5 four
6–7 8 a.m.
8 *following in the exact footprints of the narrator to make the going easier*
9 He thought that he was going to die.
10–11 'as high as a barn'; 'as broad as a house'
12–13 *The snow in the passage comes down in small flakes but very close-packed together. The March snowflakes are much bigger.*
14 There was 'some laughter'.
15 *the corner of the field at the eastern end where the great white billow of snow was*
16 sounds of sheep (bleating) under the snow
17 *a great deal of struggling and sinking in the snow*
18 *our flock was penned in*
19 *without any let-up*
20–21 'pelting pitiless arrows'; 'pointed with barbs of frost'
22–23 *For people who had no sheep, the snow was not a threat to their livelihood and they could just enjoy the sight.*
24–25 *The narrator says that there was 'no room between them' (the flakes) and 'so far at least as the weather permitted any sight at all'.*
26 *as if their lives depended on finding the sheep; the men made their living as sheep farmers and if the sheep died in the snow, their livelihoods would be ruined*
27–30 *(a) excited, willing: 'followed us cheerfully, leaping out of the depth'*
(b) distressed, frantic: 'began to scratch at once, and to howl'
31–32 *Watch knew that the sheep he was in charge of were buried in the snow and that he was powerless to do anything; his work had been taken away from him.*
33–35 *each man dug into the mound from a different direction; they moved the snow behind them until they had made tunnels into the middle*
36 business
37 estuary
38 interest
39 laboratory
40 hygiene
41 circumference
42 ferocious
43 parliament
44 marriage
45 literature
46 on/upon
47 with
48 for
49 of
50 in
51 snowy
52 frosty
53 strong
54 deep
55 distant
56 charming
57 cavernous
58 cylindrical
59 burdensome
60 apathetic
61–62 extremely cold/freezing; unfriendly
63–64 *someone who displays no emotion*
65–66 *to ignore someone*
67–68 *to point out everything which could go wrong*
69–70 *to appear to be sympathetic but to make someone feel worse*
71 (c) agree to
72 (e) give attention to
73 (b) move towards each other
74 (d) agree with
75 (a) come together

76 chocolate
77 library
78 secondary
79 cemetery
80 maintenance
81 aspirin
82 rhinoceros
83 restaurant
84 buoyant
85 mackerel
86 The snow was watched by Master Sickles.
87 The snow was blown into drifts by the wind.
88 A hole was dug in the snow by each man.
89 The sheep had been buried by the snow.
90 I was followed by the other men.
91 stare
92 beach
93 pause
94 berth
95 draught
96–100 The farmers' sheep had been buried by the heavy snowfall. They'd set out to find them. All that could be heard were the dog's barks and the men's heavy breathing as they ploughed through the deep snow. They couldn't help fearing the worst.

Paper 9

1 the countryside; references to the vales, hills, lake, trees
2 [Any two from] fluttering/dancing/tossing
3 *gives the impression of going on forever; there are so many daffodils that the poet could not see where they ended*
4 ten thousand
5 the memory of the daffodils
6 they were beside the lake and among the trees
7 *gives the impression of an infinite number/countless*
8 *a collection of innumerable stars that are too faint to be seen individually*
9–10 *The movement of the daffodils appeared livelier and more energetic than the waves.*
11–12 *the repetition of 'gazed': 'I gazed – and gazed'*
13 'as a cloud'
14 suddenly
15 valleys
16 happiness
17–18 *inside, lying on his couch, feeling empty inside and thoughtful*
19–20 *the daffodils are 'dancing'; 'tossing their heads'; experiencing 'glee'*
21–22 *they have brought the poet pleasure: 'wealth' in this context is 'pleasure' rather than a monetary term*
23–24 *memory; the ability to recall visual images*
25–28 *(a) gives the impression that he did not fully realise what a wonderful sight he was witnessing; 'little thought'*
(b) that recollecting the sight makes him extremely happy; 'my heart with pleasure fills'
29–31 *'Solitude' gives him the opportunity for peaceful reflection.*
32 it was
33 it is
34 is it
35 over
36 often
37 lie
38 lay
39 lay
40 laid
41 lain
42 should
43 shower
44 trowel
45 double
46 mountain
47 scowl
48 prowled
49 bountiful
50 cougar
51 goulash

52 (b) large number
53 (a) the area around the edge of something
54 (c) lively
55 (b) happiness
56 (a) happy
57 (b) merry
58 (c) sight
59 (b) thinking about nothing in particular
60 (a) thoughtful
61 (b) the state of being alone
62 vacantly   63 pensively
64 repeatedly   65 playfully
66 scornfully   67 coolly
68 gaily   69 nobly
70 clumsily   71 wearily
72–73 *however bad things are there is always some consolation to be found*
74–75 *to be under suspicion*
76–77 *to be out of touch with reality*
78–79 *to be extremely happy*
80–81 *to spoil something/to fill with gloom*
82 The poet said that he wandered lonely as a cloud.
83 His friend asked him where he had walked.
84 The poet replied that he had gone over by the lake.
85 His friend asked him if the daffodils were in bloom.
86 The poet said that thousands of them were in bloom and that they looked magnificent.
87 hard-working   88 chocolate-covered
89 evil-smelling   90 eighteen-hole
91 two-litre   92 unkind
93 unwise   94 uncertain
95 impossible   96 discontinue
97 inaccurate   98 irregular
99 immature   100 unnatural

Paper 10

1 Westmoreland
2 money/coins
3 Feast of Saint Crispian/Crispin
4 because they fought in the battle on Saint Crispian's/Crispin's day
5 *They will feel themselves the unluckiest of men that they were not in battle with their King.*
6 *if they are fated/destined to die*
7 *because he says 'I am not covetous for gold'*
8 *not brave enough to join in the fight*
9 enough
10 envious
11 I think
12 *provide food for them/have a celebration*
13–14 *Old men forget things, but those who have fought will never forget when they are old.*
15–16 *any man who fights, is wounded or dies with him in battle*
17–18 *The fewer Englishmen who fight and win, the greater the recognition for each of them will be when they secure a victory.*
19–21 *(a) any man who does not wish to fight the battle will be given money and safe passage home* (2 marks) *(b) to the army* (1 mark)

22–24 *Those who fought will be proud and joyful on the Feast of Saint Crispian/Crispin. They will proudly show their scars and recount their part in the battle.*
25–27 *'happy' here means 'fortunate/lucky' that they took part in the battle and will be honoured and remembered*
28–30 *he could be thought of as brave to go into battle with so small an army, and foolish for the same reason*
31 Saint   32 Doctor
33 Professor   34 Lieutenant
35 Reverend   36 less
37 less   38 fewer
39 less   40 fewer
41 3   42 4
43 1   44 5
45 2   46 victory
47 strength   48 gratitude
49 wisdom   50 honour
51 valour   52 heroism
53 cowardice   54 patriotism
55 humility
56 Because they fought bravely, King Henry and his army won the battle.
57 Before the battle, King Henry talked with his soldiers.
58 When the French army advanced, the soldiers were frightened.
59 Although his army was very small, the King was confident.
60 In order to tend to the wounded, the armies called a truce.
61–62 *to suffer from a number of minor mishaps at the same time*
63–64 *to be in an aggressive mood/ready for a fight*
65–66 *to have a fair/reasonable chance*
67–68 *to avoid; to keep away from*
69–70 *to have an apparent victory which, in reality, is no victory at all*
71 courteous   72 serious
73 outrageous   74 continuous
75 conscious   76 contagious
77 victorious   78 prosperous
79 simultaneous   80 miscellaneous
81–90 *[give half a mark in each question for correct opening speech marks; half a mark for correct closing speech marks; one mark for correct punctuation and positioning before/after spoken words]*
81–82 'I do not care about wealth but I do care about honour,' *said King Henry.*
83–84 'How can we win against the huge French army?' *asked Westmoreland.*
85–86 *King Henry said to his soldiers,* 'Listen to me. If any of you want to go home, you should go now.'
87–88 'If any soldier leaves the battlefield, he will be branded a coward!' *shouted Bedford.*
89–90 'All who fight with me on Saint Crispin's day will be remembered for ever!' *promised King Henry.*
91 campaign   92 parliament
93 exhaust   94 reliant
95 vacuum   96 substantial
97 buoyant   98 auxiliary
99 mistletoe   100 rhododendron

Complete each word with 'oy' or 'oi'.

42 v_____ce

43 tabl_____d

44 _____ster

45 empl_____ment

46 m_____sture

47 dec_____

48 b_____cott

49 all_____

50 expl_____t

51 embr_____l

Add the missing commas in each **sentence**.

52–53 Theseus thought he would need a helmet a shield a net and a sword to defeat the Minotaur.

54–55 'You must do as I tell you' said Ariadne 'and you will succeed.'

56–57 The Labyrinth built by Minos was the home of the Minotaur.

58 Theseus broke the Minotaur's neck killing it instantly.

59 The other victims made their way to the ship crept quietly aboard and sailed away.

Write an **adjective** based on each of these **nouns**.

60 misery _____

61 pain _____

62 monster _____

63 hunger _____

64 doom _____

Explain what these **expressions** mean.

65–66 to breathe down someone's neck

_____

67–68 to get it in the neck

_____

69–70 to stick one's neck out

_____

71–72 to be neck and neck

_____

73–74 to be up to one's neck

_____

10
E 2

Write a 'sch' word for each of these clues.

75 a place where you go to learn _____

76 a type of sailing ship _____

77 a plan showing the times for doing things _____

78 a plan to get rich quick _____

79 someone who is very learned _____

5
D 6

Complete the table.

	Adjective	Adverb	Noun
80–81	bold		
82–83	violent		
84–85	brave		
86–87	wicked		
88–89	prudent		

10
E 2

Write a **homophone** for each of these words.

90 due _____

91 court _____

92 great _____

93 canvas _____

94 manner _____

95 beat _____

6

Underline the **adjectival clause** in each **sentence**.

96 Theseus, who was the son of Aegeus, lived in Athens.

97 They sailed in a ship which had black sails.

98 Ariadne, who fell in love with Theseus, decided to help him.

99 She gave Theseus a ball of thread with which he could find his way out of the Labyrinth.

100 Theseus saw the Minotaur who was bellowing with rage.

5

Now go to the Progress Chart to record your score! **Total** 100

Paper 6

Gerald Durrell writes of his childhood in My Family and Other Animals. *In this extract he is particularly interested in the scorpions which live in the crumbling wall which surrounds the garden.*

Then one day I found a fat female scorpion in the wall, wearing what at first glance appeared to be a pale fawn fur coat. Closer inspection proved that this strange garment was made up of a mass of tiny babies clinging to the mother's back. I was enraptured by this family, and I made up my mind to smuggle them into the house and up to my bedroom so that I might keep them and watch them grow up.   5
With infinite care I manoeuvred the mother and family into a matchbox, and then hurried to the villa. It was rather unfortunate that just as I entered the door lunch should be served; however, I placed the matchbox carefully on the mantelpiece in the drawing-room, so that the scorpions should get plenty of air, and made my way to the dining-room and joined the family for the meal. Dawdling over my food,   10
feeding Roger surreptitiously under the table and listening to the family arguing, I completely forgot about my exciting new captures. At last Larry, having finished, fetched the cigarettes from the drawing room, and lying back in his chair he put one in his mouth and picked up the matchbox he had brought. Oblivious of my impending doom I watched him interestedly as, still talking glibly, he opened the matchbox.   15
   Now I maintain to this day that the female scorpion meant no harm. She was agitated and a trifle annoyed at being shut up in a matchbox for so long, and so she seized the first opportunity to escape. She hoisted herself out of the box with great rapidity, her babies clinging on desperately, and scuttled on to the back of Larry's hand. There, not quite certain what to do next, she paused, her sting curved   20
up at the ready. Larry, feeling the movement of her claws, glanced down to see what it was, and from that moment things got increasingly confused.

He uttered a roar of fright that made Lugaretzia drop a plate and brought Roger out from beneath the table, barking wildly. With a flick of his hand he sent the unfortunate scorpion flying down the table, and she landed midway between Margo and Leslie, scattering babies like confetti as she thumped on the cloth. Thoroughly enraged at this treatment, the creature sped towards Leslie, her sting quivering with emotion. Leslie leapt to his feat, overturning his chair, and flicked out desperately with his napkin, sending the scorpion rolling across the cloth towards Margo, who promptly let out a scream that any railway engine would have been proud to produce. Mother, completely bewildered by this sudden and rapid change from peace to chaos, put on her glasses and peered down the table to see what was causing the pandemonium, and at that moment Margo, in a vain attempt to stop the scorpion's advance, hurled a glass of water at it. The shower missed the animal completely, but successfully drenched Mother, who, not being able to stand cold water, promptly lost her breath and sat gasping at the end of the table, unable even to protest. The scorpion had now gone to ground under Leslie's plate while her babies swarmed wildly all over the table. Roger, mystified by the panic, but determined to do his share, ran round and round the room, barking hysterically.

'It's that bloody boy again…' bellowed Larry.

'Look out! Look out! They're coming!' screamed Margo.

'All we need is a book,' roared Leslie; 'don't panic, hit 'em with a book.'

'What on earth's the *matter* with you all?' Mother kept imploring, mopping her glasses.

'It's that bloody boy… he'll kill the lot of us… Look at the table… knee deep in scorpions…'

'Quick… quick… do something… Look out, look out!'

'Stop screeching and get a book, for God's sake… You're worse than the dog… Shut *up*, Roger…'

'By the Grace of God I wasn't bitten…'

'Look out… there's another one… Quick… quick…'

'Oh, shut up and get me a book or something…'

'But *how* did the scorpions get on the table, dear?'

'That bloody boy… Every matchbox in the house is a deathtrap…'

'Look out, it's coming towards me… Quick, quick, do something…'

'Hit it with your knife… *your knife*… Go on, hit it…'

Since no one had bothered to explain things to him, Roger was under the mistaken impression that the family were being attacked, and that it was his duty to defend them. As Lugaretzia was the only stranger in the room, he came to the logical conclusion that she must be the responsible party, so he bit her in the ankle. This did not help matters very much.

By the time a certain amount of order had been restored, all the baby scorpions had hidden themselves under various plates and bits of cutlery. Eventually, after impassioned pleas on my part, backed up by Mother, Leslie's suggestion that the whole lot be slaughtered was quashed. While the family, still simmering with rage and fright, retired to the drawing-room, I spent half an hour rounding up the babies, picking them up in a teaspoon, and returning them to their mother's back. Then I carried them outside on a saucer and, with the utmost reluctance, released them on the garden wall. Roger and I went and spent the afternoon on the hillside, for I felt it would be prudent to allow the family to have a siesta before seeing them again.

From *My Family and Other Animals* by Gerald Durrell

Answer these questions.

1 Where did the author find the scorpions?

_____

2 Why was it 'unfortunate' that lunch was ready just as the author returned to the house?

_____

_____

3 Whose hand did the scorpion climb onto?

_____

4 What **simile** does the author use to show what happened to the baby scorpions when Larry flicked them with his napkin?

_____

5 What was Margo's scream compared to?

_____

6 How did Leslie propose to get rid of the scorpions?

_____

7–8 Give two reasons why the female scorpion was keen to get out of the matchbox.

_____

_____

9 How do you know that this was not the first time the author had kept creatures in matchboxes?

_____

10–11 Give two reasons why you can tell that Lugaretzia was not one of the family.

_____

_____

12–14 Explain these **phrases** in your own words.

(a)   'the mistaken impression' (lines 56–7)

_____

(b)   'vain attempt' (line 33)

_____

(c) 'gone to ground' (line 37)

_____

15 How do you know that getting the scorpions onto the saucer was a difficult job?

_____

_____

16 Why did the author think it was a good idea to spend the afternoon on the hillside?

_____

17–19 What does the description of collecting up the scorpions in the last paragraph tell you about the author's attitude to them? Give examples from the passage in your answer.

_____

_____

_____

20–21 What do these words mean?

'enraptured' (line 4) _____

'swarmed' (line 38) _____

22–24 Find three pieces of evidence in the passage which show you that the author was very interested in animals.

_____

_____

_____

25–26 In the dialogue section of the passage, the author rarely identifies the speakers. What impression does this give the reader?

_____

_____

Match each word with its **definition** as used in the passage.

27 surreptitiously _____ (a) unlucky

28 oblivious _____ (b) wise

26

E 2

29	rapidity	_____	(c)	secretly
30	unfortunate	_____	(d)	puzzled
31	bewildered	_____	(e)	confusion
32	pandemonium	_____	(f)	speed
33	imploring	_____	(g)	dismissed
34	quashed	_____	(h)	unaware
35	prudent	_____	(i)	begging

Write a **homophone** for each of these words by adding a silent letter.

36 night	_____	37 rap	_____
38 retch	_____	39 new	_____
40 plum	_____	41 sent	_____
42 ring	_____	43 rite	_____

Underline the **verbs** in each **sentence**.

44 The family were having lunch.

45 He had been collecting insects for many years.

46 The family would have liked a peaceful meal.

47 The scorpion might have been killed.

48 He will hide his matchboxes in the future.

Complete each word with the **suffix** 'sure' or 'ture'.

49 disclo_____	50 tempera_____
51 lei_____	52 infrastruc_____
53 architec_____	54 carica_____
55 compo_____	56 manufac_____
57 cen_____	58 mois_____

9

8

D 6

5

E 2

10

Explain what these **expressions** mean.

59–60 to bite the hand that feeds you

_____

_____

61–62 to be hand in glove with someone

_____

_____

63–64 to hold the whip hand

_____

_____

65–66 to be a dab hand at something

_____

_____

67–68 to get the situation in hand

_____

_____

10

D 6

Replace the words in bold with a suitable **pronoun**.

69 The scorpion landed between **Margo and Leslie**.

_____

70 The matchbox belonged to **Larry**.

_____

71 **The scorpion** was agitated and annoyed.

_____

72 Roger bit **Lugaretzia**.

_____

73 He kept out of **the family's** way until later in the day.

_____

5

Write the **abstract noun** which can be made from each of these **adverbs**.

Adverb	Abstract noun
74 desperately	_____
75 completely	_____
76 promptly	_____
77 hysterically	_____
78 generously	_____

Write a word or **phrase** to explain the meaning of:

79 back down _____

80 back up _____

81 back off _____

82 back out _____

83 backbite _____

Add a **prefix** and a **suffix** to each **root word** to make a new word. Remember to make any necessary spelling changes.

Prefix	Root word	Suffix
84 _____	friendly	_____
85 _____	stress	_____
86 _____	turn	_____
87 _____	accurate	_____
88 _____	ordinary	_____
89 _____	move	_____

Complete each **sentence** with 'like' or 'as'.

90 Margo, _____ the rest of the family, was frightened of the scorpion.

91 Some creatures, such _____ scorpions, can be dangerous.

92 Some insects, such _____ bees, have stings.

93 He didn't stop bringing creatures into the house _____ he said he would.

94 _____ he expected, he was in a lot of trouble.

Write the word class of each word in bold.

95 I **scream** when I see a spider. _____

96 The **scream** echoed through the house. _____

97 He stayed indoors in the **cold** weather. _____

98 There is no cure for the common **cold**. _____

99 I **garden** at the weekend. _____

100 The **garden** wall was covered in insects. _____

6

Now go to the Progress Chart to record your score! Total 100

Paper 7

The Darkling Thrush

I leant upon a coppice gate
   When Frost was spectre-grey,
And Winter's dregs made desolate
   The weakening eye of day.
The tangled bine-stems scored the sky   5
   Like strings of broken lyres,
And all mankind that haunted nigh
   Had sought their household fires.

The land's sharp features seemed to be
   The Century's corpse outleant,   10
His crypt the cloudy canopy,
   The wind his death-lament.
The ancient pulse of germ and birth
   Was shrunken hard and dry,
And every spirit upon earth   15
   Seemed fervourless as I.

At once a voice arose among
   The bleak twigs overhead
In a full-hearted evensong

Of joy illimited; 20
An aged thrush, frail, gaunt, and small,
In blast-beruffled plume,
Had chosen thus to fling his soul
Upon the growing gloom.

So little cause for carollings 25
Of such ecstatic sound
Was written on terrestrial things
Afar or nigh around,
That I could think there trembled through
His happy good-night air 30
Some blessed Hope, whereof he knew
And I was unaware.

by Thomas Hardy

Answer these questions.

1 At what time of the year is the poem set?

_____

2 How do you know that the poet is alone?

_____

3 Explain in your own words: 'The ancient pulse of germ and birth'.

_____

_____

4 What does the poet hear in 'the growing gloom'?

_____

5 Find two **adjectives** which the poet uses to describe the bird.

_____

6 Explain in your own words: 'Afar or nigh around'.

_____

7–8 At what time of the day is the poem set? Quote to support your answer.

_____

9–10 Explain these **phrases** in your own words:

(a) 'spectre-grey'

_____

(b) 'blast-beruffled plume'

_____

11–12 The poet describes himself as 'fervourless'. How do you think he is feeling?

_____

_____

13–14 At first, why is the poet puzzled by the sound he hears?

_____

_____

15–16 How does the poet explain the bird's joyful singing? Quote to support your answer.

_____

_____

17–19 The poem was written at the very end of the 19th century. Find three **phrases** in the poem which support this.

_____

_____

_____

20 Which **simile** does the poet use to describe the bine-stems?

_____

21–22 Write in your own words why the **simile** is effective.

_____

_____

23–25 The landscape affects the poet's mood. Pick out three words or **phrases** which show how gloomy the surroundings were.

_____

_____

_____

26–28 Find three **phrases** from the poem which show that the bird was feeling very differently from the poet.

_____

_____

_____

◯ 28

E 2

Complete each word with 's' or 'c'.

29 analy_____e

30 audien_____e

31 deci_____ion

32 eviden_____e

33 ne_____essary

34 sin_____erely

35 per_____pective

36 re_____ipe

37 _____itizen

38 sen_____or

◯ 10

Explain what these **expressions** mean.

39–40 to sail close to the wind

_____

41–42 to get wind of something

_____

43–44 to get a second wind

_____

45–46 to whistle in the wind

_____

47–48 to take the wind out of someone's sails

_____

◯ 10

D 2

Underline the **adverbial phrase** in each **sentence**.

49 I walked over the fields in the early evening.

50 The wind whistled through the trees with a low moan.

51 I saw a thrush sitting on the highest branch.

52 The bird sang loudly and joyfully.

53 It began to snow so I walked back in a hurry.

◯ 5

Add the missing hyphen in each **sentence**.

54 Thomas Hardy is a world famous author.

55 He continued to write poetry until his mid eighties.

56 He built a strange looking house called Max Gate.

57 *The Darkling Thrush* is one of his best known poems.

58 Some people thought several of his stories were far fetched.

Complete each word with 'i' or 'y'.

59 ph_____sical

60 acr_____lic

61 br_____ef

62 d_____nasty

63 h_____giene

64 pol_____ester

65 vitam_____n

66 m_____th

67 rh_____me

68 d_____namics

Match each word with its **definition** as used in the poem.

69 coppice _____ (a) barren

70 desolate _____ (b) thin and haggard

71 lyres _____ (c) group of small trees

72 gaunt _____ (d) of the earth

73 terrestrial _____ (e) musical instruments

Circle the **adjective** in each group of four which is the *opposite* of the other three.

74 cloudy	overcast	grey	clear
75 abundant	plentiful	meagre	copious
76 ecstatic	doleful	delighted	joyful
77 infirm	robust	sturdy	stalwart
78 rich	wealthy	destitute	affluent

Make each word into its opposite by adding a **prefix**.

79 legal   _____   80 mature   _____

81 natural   _____   82 numerable   _____

83 regular   _____   84 moral   _____

85 legible   _____   86 rational   _____

87 mobile   _____   88 logical   _____

E 2

10

Change these **sentences** from **singular** to **plural**.

D 6
E 2

89 I leant upon a coppice gate.

_____

90 He was unhappy and lonely in the field.

_____

91 The bird sang his song from high in the tree.

_____

92 The poet does not know why the bird is singing so ecstatically.

_____

4

Circle the correct form of the word in brackets in each **sentence**.

E 2

93 My (advise/advice) is to stay away from the car park.

94 I (advise/advice) you to have breakfast before you go.

95 The permit will (license/licence) you to fish for the day.

96 The (license/licence) will let you fish for the day.

97 You can (practise/practice) for the match on Friday.

98 Choir (practise/practice) will be at six.

99 The ancient (prophecy/prophesy) predicted terrible plagues.

100 The wizard comes here to (prophecy/prophesy).

8

This extract from Lorna Doone *describes when farmers had to go out and rescue sheep buried under heavy snowfalls.*

It must have snowed most wonderfully to have made that depth of covering in about eight hours. For one of Master Stickles' men, who had been out all the night, said that no snow began to fall until nearly midnight. And here it was, blocking up the doors, stopping the ways, and the water-courses, and making it very much worse to walk than in a saw-pit newly used. However we trudged along in a line; I first, 5 and the other men after me; trying to keep my track, but finding legs and strength not up to it. Most of all, John Fry was groaning; certain that his time was come, and sending messages to his wife, and blessings to his children. For all this time it was snowing harder than it ever had snowed before, so far as a man might guess at it; and the leaden depth of the sky came down, like a mine turned upside down 10 on us. Not that the flakes were so very large; for I have seen much larger flakes in a shower of March, while sowing peas; but that there was no room between them, neither any relaxing, nor any change of direction.

Watch, like a good and faithful dog, followed us cheerfully, leaping out of the depth, which took him over his back and ears already, even in the level places; 15 while in the drifts he might have sunk to any distance out of sight, and never found his way up again. However, we helped him now and then, especially through the gaps and gateways, and so after a deal of floundering, some laughter and a little swearing, we all came safe to the lower meadow, where most of our flock was hurdled.

But behold, there was no flock at all! None, I mean, to be seen anywhere, only 20 at one corner of the field, by the eastern end, where the snow drove in, a great white billow, as high as a barn and as broad as a house… And all the while from the smothering sky, more and more fiercely at every blast, came the pelting pitiless arrows, winged with murky white, and pointed with barbs of frost.

But although, for people who had no sheep, the sight was a very fine one (so 25 far at least as the weather permitted any sight at all); yet for us, with our flock beneath it, this great mount had but little charm. Watch began to scratch at once, and to howl along the side of it; he knew that his charge was buried there, and his business taken from him. But we four men set to in earnest, digging with all our might and main, shovelling away at the great white pile, and fetching it into the 30 meadow. Each man made for himself a cave, scooping at the soft cold flux, which slid upon him at every stroke, and throwing it out behind him, in piles of castled fancy. At last we drove our tunnels in (for we worked indeed for the lives of us), and all converging towards the middle, held our tools and listened.

From *Lorna Doone* by R D Blackmore

Answer these questions.

1 At what time had the snow started to fall?

_____

2 Find two **adjectives** which the author uses to describe Watch.

_____

3 What is the **collective noun** for a group of sheep?

_____

4 Where were the farmers going to look for their sheep?

_____

5 How many farmers were going to look for their sheep?

_____

6–7 What time is it at the beginning of the passage?

_____

8 The narrator says that the other men were 'trying to keep my track' (line 6). What were the other men doing and why?

_____

9 John Fry was 'certain that his time had come'. What does this mean?

_____

10–11 Find two **similes** which the author uses to describe the 'great, white billow'.

_____

12–13 What is the difference between the snow in this passage and the snow in early spring?

_____

14 How can you tell that the men's walk was not completely miserable?

_____

15 Where did the author think the flock was in the field?

_____

16 When the men stopped digging, what were they listening for?

_____

17–19 What do these **phrases** mean?

'a deal of floundering' (line 18)   _____

'our flock was hurdled' (line 19)   _____

'neither any relaxing' (line 13)   _____

20–21 Find two descriptions of the snow which suggest that the narrator thought of it as a weapon being hurled at them.

_____

_____

22–23 Why do you think so much snow was a fine sight 'for people who had no sheep'?

_____

_____

24–25 How do you know that the snow was falling so heavily that the farmers had difficulty in seeing? Find two **phrases** that show this.

_____

_____

26 What does the narrator mean when he says 'for we worked for the very lives of us'?

_____

_____

27–30 How is Watch feeling when:

(a) they set off to look for the sheep?

(b) they reached the corner of the field?

Quote from the passage to support your answer.

(a) _____

_____

(b) _____

_____

31–32 What does the author mean when he says that Watch 'knew that his charge was buried there, and his business taken from him' (lines 28–9)?

_____

_____

33–35 Explain in your own words how the farmers tried to dig out the sheep.

_____

_____

_____

35

Circle the unstressed vowels in each word.

E 2

36 business _____

37 estuary _____

38 interest _____

39 laboratory _____

40 hygiene _____

41 circumference _____

42 ferocious _____

43 parliament _____

44 marriage _____

45 literature _____

10

Complete each **expression** with a **preposition**.

D 6

46 Can I depend _____ you?

47 I am satisfied _____ my work.

48 He had a good ear _____ music.

49 She was worthy _____ great praise.

50 She decided to confide _____ her friend.

5

Make an **adjective** from each of these **nouns**.

D 6

51 snow _____

52 frost _____

53 strength _____

54 depth _____

55 distance _____

56 charm _____

57 cavern _____

58 cylinder _____

59 burden _____

60 apathy _____

10

Explain what these **expressions** mean.

61–62 as cold as ice

_____

63–64 a cold-blooded person

_____

65–66 to give someone the cold shoulder

_____

67–68 to pour cold water on something

_____

69–70 to give cold comfort

_____

10

E 2

Match each word with the correct **definition**.

71 consent   _____   (a) come together

72 concentrate   _____   (b) move towards each other

73 converge   _____   (c) agree to

74 concur   _____   (d) agree with

75 convene   _____   (e) give attention to

5

E 2

Complete each word with the correct vowel.

76 choc_____late   **77** libr_____ry

78 second_____ry   **79** cemet_____ry

80 maint_____nance   **81** asp_____rin

82 rhinocer_____s   **83** resta_____rant

84 b_____oyant   **85** mack_____rel

10

Change each of the active sentences into passive sentences.

D 1

86 Master Sickles watched the snow.

_____

87 The wind blew the snow into drifts.

_____

88 Each man dug a hole in the snow.

_____

89 The snow had buried the sheep.

_____

90 The other men followed me.

_____

5

E 2

Write a **homophone** for each of these words.

91 stair   _____

92 beech   _____

93 paws   _____

94 birth   _____

95 draft   _____

5

D 5

Rewrite the passage in the context of the extract, adding the missing apostrophes.

96–100 The farmers sheep had been buried by the heavy snowfall. Theyd set out to find them. All that could be heard were the dogs barks and the mens heavy breathing as they ploughed through the deep snow. They couldnt help fearing the worst.

_____

_____

_____

_____

5

Now go to the Progress Chart to record your score!   Total   100

I wandered lonely as a cloud

I wandered lonely as a cloud
That floats on high o'er vales and hills,
When all at once I saw a crowd,
A host of golden daffodils;
Beside the lake, beneath the trees,   5
Fluttering and dancing in the breeze.

Continuous as the stars that shine
And twinkle on the milky way,
They stretched in never-ending line
Along the margin of the bay: 10
Ten thousand saw I at a glance,
Tossing their heads in sprightly dance.

The waves beside them danced; but they
Out-did the sparkling waves in glee:
A poet could not but be gay,   15
In such a jocund company:
I gazed – and gazed – but little thought
What wealth the show to me had brought:

For oft, when on my couch I lie
In vacant or in pensive mood,   20
They flash upon that inward eye
Which is the bliss of solitude;
And then my heart with pleasure fills,
And dances with the daffodils.

by William Wordsworth

Answer these questions.

1 Do you think the poet is walking in a town or in the countryside? Give a reason for your answer.

_____

_____

2 Find two **verbs** which show how the daffodils moved.

_____

3 What does the **phrase** 'never-ending' tell you about the daffodils?

_____

4 How many daffodils does the poet think he saw?

_____

5 What makes the poet's heart fill with 'pleasure'?

_____

6 Where exactly were the daffodils?

_____

7 What does the line 'Continuous as the stars that shine' (line 7) tell you about the daffodils?

_____

_____

8 What is the 'milky way' (line 8)?

_____

9–10 What does the poet mean when he says that the daffodils 'out-did' the waves?

_____

_____

11–12 How do you know that the poet spent a long time looking at the daffodils?

_____

_____

13 Find an example of a **simile** in the poem.

_____

14–16 What do these words and **phrases** in the poem mean?

'all at once' (line 3) _____

'vales' (line 2) _____

'bliss' (line 22) _____

17–18 Where is the poet when he thinks about the daffodils and what kind of state is he in?

_____

19–20 Explain in your own words how the poet makes the daffodils seem human. Give examples from the poem.

_____

_____

_____

21–22 In what way do you think the sight of the daffodils brought 'wealth' to the poet?

_____

_____

23–24 Explain what you think the poet means by 'inward eye'.

_____

_____

25–28 What did the poet feel about the daffodils:

(a)   when he first saw them? (*2 marks*)

(b)   when he thought about them later? (*2 marks*)

Quote from the poem to support your answer.

(a) _____

_____

(b) _____

_____

29–31 What do you think makes 'solitude' so blissful for the poet?

_____

_____

31

Write these old-fashioned words in full.

32 'twas   _____   **33** 'tis   _____

34 is't   _____   **35** o'er   _____

5

36 oft   _____

56

Complete each **sentence** with one of the following:

E 2

lie　　　　**lay**　　　　**lain**　　　　**laid**

37 I like to _____ on the grass and look at the clouds.

38 I _____ down because I had a headache.

39 Dad asked me to _____ the table.

40 The army _____ down its weapons.

41 The old watch must have _____ in the drawer for years.

5

Add 'ou' or 'ow' to complete each word.

E 2

42 sh_____ld

43 sh_____er

44 tr_____el

45 d_____ble

46 m_____ntain

47 sc_____l

48 pr_____led

49 b_____ntiful

50 c_____gar

51 g_____lash

10

Circle the **definition** which is closest in meaning to the word in bold as it is used in the poem.

E 2

52 host

  (a) person who invites guests to their house

  (b) large number

  (c) person who introduces a television show

53 margin

  (a) the area around the edge of something

  (b) the empty space at the side of a page

  (c) an amount of space that is more than you need

54 sprightly

  (a) goblin-like

  (b) mournful

  (c) lively

55 glee

    (a)   soft light

    (b)   happiness

    (c)   spite

56 gay

    (a)   happy

    (b)   thoughtful

    (c)   sad

57 jocund

    (a)   large

    (b)   merry

    (c)   colourful

58 show

    (a)   entertainment

    (b)   walk

    (c)   sight

59 vacant

    (a)   empty-headed

    (b)   thinking about nothing in particular

    (c)   sorrowful

60 pensive

    (a)   thoughtful

    (b)   having money

    (c)   angry

61 solitude

    (a)   the state of being abandoned

    (b)   the state of being alone

    (c)   the state of being miserable

10

Make an **adverb** from each of these **adjectives**.

D 6

62 vacant _____

63 pensive _____

64 repeated _____

65 playful _____

66 scornful _____

67 cool _____

68 gay _____

69 noble _____

70 clumsy _____

71 weary _____

10

Explain what these **expressions** mean.

72–73 every cloud has a silver lining

_____

74–75 to be under a cloud

_____

76–77 to have one's head in the clouds

_____

78–79 to be on cloud nine

_____

80–81 to cast a cloud over

_____

10

Change each of the **sentences** from **direct** to **reported speech**.

D 12

82 'I wandered lonely as a cloud,' said the poet.

_____

83 'Where did you walk?' asked his friend.

_____

84 The poet replied, 'I went over by the lake.'

_____

85 'Were the daffodils in bloom?' asked his friend.

_____

86 'Yes. Thousands of them,' the poet said. 'They looked magnificent.'

_____

Use a hyphenated compound adjective to complete each **sentence**.

87 A person who works hard is a _____ _____ person.

88 Biscuits covered in chocolate are _____ _____ biscuits.

89 Medicine with an evil smell is an _____ _____ medicine.

90 A golf course with eighteen holes is an _____ _____ golf course.

91 A bottle that holds two litres is a _____ _____ bottle.

Write an **antonym** for each word by adding a **prefix**.

92 kind _____

93 wise _____

94 certain _____

95 possible _____

96 continue _____

97 accurate _____

98 regular _____

99 mature _____

100 natural _____

This extract from Henry V by William Shakespeare takes place on the eve of battle. The English are about to face the French. The Duke of Westmoreland suggests that they need a bigger army. King Henry replies...

If we are mark'd to die, we are enow
To do our country loss; and if to live,
The fewer men the greater share of honour.
God's will! I pray thee, wish not one man more.
By Jove, I am not covetous for gold;   5
Nor care I who doth feed upon my cost:
It yearns me not if men my garments wear;
Such outward things dwell not in my desires:
But if it be a sin to covet honour,
I am the most offending soul alive.   10
No, faith, my coz, wish not a man from England:
God's peace! I would not lose so great an honour,
As one man more, methinks, would share from me,
For the best hope I have. O do not wish one more!
Rather proclaim it, Westmoreland, through my host,   15
That he which hath no stomach to this fight,
Let him depart; his passport shall be made,
And crowns for convoy put into his purse:
We would not die in that man's company
That fears his fellowship to die with us.   20
This day is call'd the Feast of Crispian:
He that outlives this day, and comes safe home,
Will stand a tip-toe when this day is nam'd,
And rouse him at the name of Crispian.
He that shall live this day, and see old age,   25
Will yearly on the vigil feast his neighbours,
And say, To-morrow is Saint Crispian:
Then will he strip his sleeve and show his scars,
And say, These wounds I had on Crispin's day.
Old men forget; yet all shall be forgot,   30
But he'll remember with advantages
What feats he did that day: then shall our names,
Familiar in their mouths as household words, –
Harry the King, Bedford and Exeter,
Warwick and Talbot, Salisbury and Gloster –   35
Be in their flowing cups freshly remember'd.
This story shall the good man teach his son;
And Crispin Crispian shall ne'er go by,
From this day to the ending of the world, –
But we in it shall be remember'd,   40
We few, we happy few, we band of brothers;
For he to-day that sheds his blood with me

Shall be my brother; be he ne'er so vile,
This day shall gentle his condition:
And gentlemen in England now a-bed 45
Shall think themselves accurs'd they were not here,
And hold their manhoods cheap whiles any speaks
That fought with us upon Saint Crispin's day.

Answer these questions.

1 Who is King Henry talking to?

_____

2 The men who go home will be given 'crowns' (line 18). What does this mean?

_____

3 What feast day is it?

_____

4 Why does the King think that his name and those of Bedford, Exeter, Warwick, Talbot, Salisbury and Gloster will be remembered?

_____

_____

5 How will 'gentlemen in England now a-bed' (line 45) feel when the battle is talked of in the future?

_____

_____

6 Explain the meaning of: 'If we are mark'd to die' (line 1).

_____

_____

7 How do you know that the King is not bothered about being rich? Give evidence from the text.

_____

_____

8 Explain the **expression**: 'no stomach to this fight' (line 16).

_____

_____

9–11 What do these words mean?

'enow' (line 1) _____

'covetous' (line 5) _____

'methinks' (line 13) _____

12 On the anniversary of the battle, a soldier who fought with the King will 'feast his neighbours' (line 26). What does this mean?

_____

_____

13–14 What will the difference be in the future between most old men and those old men who fought in the battle when they were young?

_____

_____

15–16 Explain in your own words whom Henry will consider his 'brother'.

_____

_____

17–18 Explain what the King means when he says: 'The fewer men the greater share of honour'.

_____

_____

19–21 Henry says, 'Rather proclaim it, Westmoreland, through my host'.

Explain in your own words:

(a)   what Henry wants proclaimed.

_____

_____

(b)   to whom he wants Westmoreland to 'proclaim it'.

_____

_____

22–24 Explain in your own words how those who fought and came 'safe home' will behave, each year, on the anniversary of the battle.

_____

_____

25–27 Explain in your own words why the King calls those with him, 'We few, we happy few' (line 41).

_____

_____

28–30 Henry could be considered a brave man or a foolish man for the same reason. Why?

_____

_____

30

D 10

Write these **abbreviations** in full.

    31 St. Christopher   _____

    32 Dr. Green   _____

    33 Prof. West   _____

    34 Lieut. Sharp   _____

    35 Rev. Jones   _____

5

E 2

Complete each **sentence** with 'less' or 'fewer'.

    36 I wish you would make _____ noise!

    37 Please put _____ water in the kettle.

    38 There are _____ members of the club this year.

    39 You have been _____ successful this time.

    40 We have had _____ sunny days this month than last month.

5

E 2

Match each word with its correct **definition** as used in Henry's speech. Write the correct number in the space.

    41 covet   _____   (a) travel

    42 offending   _____   (b) humble

43	convoy	_____	(c)	desire
44	feats	_____	(d)	sinning
45	vile	_____	(e)	deeds

D 6

5

Make **abstract nouns** from these **adjectives**.

	Adjective	Abstract noun
46	victorious	_____
47	strong	_____
48	grateful	_____
49	wise	_____
50	honourable	_____
51	valiant	_____
52	heroic	_____
53	cowardly	_____
54	patriotic	_____
55	humble	_____

10

D 1
D 2

Rewrite each **sentence** with the **adverbial clause** at the beginning.

56 King Henry and his army won the battle because they fought bravely.

_____

57 Henry talked with his soldiers before the battle.

_____

58 The soldiers were frightened when the French army advanced.

_____

59 The King was confident although his army was very small.

_____

60 The armies agreed a truce in order to tend to the wounded.

_____

5

Explain what these **expressions** mean.

61–62 to be in the wars

_____

63–64 to be on the warpath

_____

65–66 to have a fighting chance

_____

67–68 to fight shy of

_____

69–70 to have a pyrrhic victory

_____

10

E 2

Add 'ous', 'ious', or 'eous' to complete each word.

71 court_____   **72** ser_____

73 outrag_____   **74** continu_____

75 consc_____   **76** contag_____

77 victor_____   **78** prosper_____

79 simultan_____   **80** miscellan_____

10

D 12

Rewrite each of these **reported speech sentences** as **direct speech**.

81–82 King Henry said that he didn't care about wealth but he did care about honour.

_____

_____

83–84 Westmoreland asked how they could win against the huge French army.

_____

_____

85–86 The King said that his soldiers must listen to him. If any of them wanted to go home, they could go now.

_____

_____

87–88 Bedford shouted that if any soldier left the battlefield, he would be branded a coward.

_____

_____

89–90 King Henry promised that all who fought with him on Saint Crispin's day would be remembered for ever.

_____

_____

10

Fill the gaps to complete the spelling of each word.

91 campai___n

92 parl___ament

93 ex___aust

94 reli___nt

95 vac___um

96 substan___ial

97 b___oyant

98 auxil___ary

99 mis___letoe

100 rhod___dendron

10

Now go to the Progress Chart to record your score!   Total   100

Progress Chart English 12⁺-13⁺ years

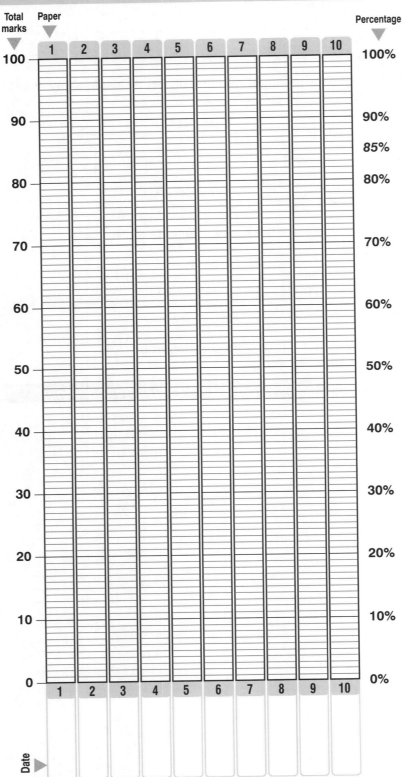

When you've finished the book use the *Next Steps Planner*